*Mercier Press is the oldest independent Irish
publishing house and has published books in the
fields of history, literature, folklore, music, art,
humour, drama, politics, current affairs, law
and religion. It was founded in 1944 by John
and Mary Feehan.*

*In the building up of a country
few needs are as great as that of a publishing
house which would make the people proud of
their past, and proud of themselves as a people
capable of inspiring and supporting a world of
books which was their very own. Mercier Press
has tried to be that publishing house. On the
occasion of our fiftieth anniversary we thank
the many writers and readers who have
supported us and contributed to our success.*

*We face our second half-century
with confidence.*

The Editor

Colm Keane is a graduate of Trinity College, Dublin (BA Econ, MA) and Georgetown University, Washington DC (MA Econ). He joined RTE in 1977 where he presented 'Public Account' and worked as a reporter on 'Today Tonight'. He is currently a senior producer with RTE Radio One, where he won a Jacob's Award for his 'American Profiles' series. He is editor of **Mental Health in Ireland** *(published in 1991) and the best selling book* **The Jobs Crisis** *(published in 1993).*

NERVOUS BREAKDOWN

EDITED

by

COLM KEANE

Published in association with
Radio Telefís Éireann

MERCIER PRESS

MERCIER PRESS
PO Box 5, 5 French Church Street, Cork and
24 Lower Abbey Street, Dublin 1

© The contributors, 1994

ISBN 1 85635 080 0

A CIP is available for this book from the British Library.

Printed in Ireland by Colour Books Ltd.

CONTENTS

List of Contributors

Colm Keane	Senior Producer, Radio Telefís Éireann
Anthony Clare	Medical Director, St Patrick's Hospital, Dublin; Clinical Professor of Psychiatry, Trinity College, Dublin
Anthony Bates	Senior Clinical Psychologist, St James's Hospital, Dublin
Marie Murray	Clinical Psychologist and Psychotherapist in private practice, Stillorgan, Co. Dublin
Edward Hogan	Senior Clinical Psychologist, St Anne's Hospital and Clinic, Cork
Frank O'Donoghue	Consultant Psychiatrist, St Patrick's Hospital, Dublin
Gillian Moore-Groarke	Director/Consultant Psychologist, St Francis Medical Out-Patient Centre, Cork
Richard Booth	Senior Clinical Psychologist, St Patrick's Hospital, Dublin
Tom Kelly	Psychosexual Therapist and Medical Co-ordinator, Family Planning Services Ltd
Andrew Honeyman	Executive Director, Rutland Centre Ltd, Dublin

Mary McGoldrick	Behaviour Nurse Therapist, St Patrick's Hospital, Dublin
Paul Andrews	Director, St Declan's Child Guidance Centre, Dublin
Fred Lowe	Senior Clinical Psychologist, Eastern Health Board
Thérèse Brady	Director of Postgraduate Training in Clinical Psychology, University College, Dublin
Eunice McCarthy	Professor of Social and Organisational Psychology, University College, Dublin
Órla O'Neill	Head Occupational Therapist, St John of God Hospital, Stillorgan, Co. Dublin
Aidan Moran	Lecturer in Psychology, Director of Research Laboratory, University College, Dublin

INTRODUCTION

COLM KEANE

THIS BOOK IS AIMED at a wide range of people – those suffering from 'bad nerves', or those who have had or are having the symptoms of 'nervous breakdown'.

You may qualify if you complain of being agitated, panicky, jittery, edgy, tense or nervous. You may feel down, unhappy, black, hopeless. You may suffer from anger, despair, guilt, irritability, hostility.

You may complain of exhaustion, lethargy, fatigue, headache, difficulty in sleeping, palpitations, difficulty in concentrating or thinking, problems with weight, a loss of interest in life, a desire to commit suicide.

These symptoms may affect you at school, at work, at home or in your social and interpersonal relationships. They may cause a multitude of physical symptoms, accounting for a major proportion of visits to your doctor.

If your symptoms are mild you may refer to them as just 'bad nerves'. If they are more severe or last a long time you may believe that you have had or are having a 'nervous breakdown'.

Whatever the cause, the damage to you can be distressing, debilitating, emotionally disturbing. The ultimate consequence can be burnout or psychological collapse.

THIS BOOK IS A companion to the RTE Radio One series 'Nervous Breakdown'. It was my intention that the radio programmes would provide listeners with the human voice of 'breakdown'. With this in mind, each programme contains a case history describing his or her experience with a wide range of psychological problems. The book, on the other hand, provides a more comprehensive treatment of the subject matter than a series of half-hour programmes would allow. It is hoped that, in this way, those who are interested can avail of a more detailed point of reference and a useful information source.

The chapter headings and programme titles are chosen to reflect many of the commonly accepted categories of 'breakdown'. Most are caused by stress and anxiety. Some are related to life events. Others are linked to problems with relationships or the various addictions.

As Anthony Clare points out, 'nervous breakdown' ultimately covers all forms of mental illness and does not describe any nor discriminate between any. To this extent it encompasses a broad spectrum of elements that characterise mental ill-health. If only for this reason, the following chapters provide an interesting insight into the extent of psychological distress and mental ill-health in this country.

THE SUDDEN PANIC ATTACKS, the choking, dizzy, sweating, palpitating fears that affect two in every one hundred people each year are examined by Richard Booth. He describes how one woman sufferer would drive her husband to work and wait for him in the car park all day. 'This secrecy and misery continued for many weeks and shows the terror that can be induced from the prospect of having a panic on one's own,' he concludes.

Then there is obsessive compulsive disorder, with its rituals, bizarre behaviour and intrusive thoughts, affecting one out of every forty people. Frank O'Donoghue describes how some sufferers wash their hands up to 150 times a day or operate up to 500 checks each night before going to bed. This is, he says, 'as crippling in its severe manifestations as some psychotic conditions such as schizophrenia'.

Anthony Bates tells us about the 300,000 sufferers from depression in Ireland. These are people experiencing the collapse of their self-esteem, a paralysis of their ability to cope and a gradual withdrawal into personal despair. 'I am struck by how confused and demoralised they are by the experience,' he adds.

And the phobias? There are more than 300 different phobias. They range from relatively uncommon complaints like brontophobia (fear of thunder) and trichophobia (fear of hair) right through to fear of mice, spiders, heights, open places, even people.

Some two to three percent of the population suffer from blood phobias, Mary McGoldrick explains. A further two percent suffer from social phobias. And agoraphobia (literally, fear of the market place) is the commonest phobia, affecting four times more women than men.

'For people who suffer from any of these phobic conditions, feelings of guilt, hopelessness, helplessness and worthlessness are common,' she concludes.

INSOMNIA, ACCORDING TO MARIE MURRAY, is one of the most common complaints in general medical practice and is estimated to occur in approximately 30% of the population. This is one of the many sleep disorders she examines in her chapter. 'Sleep problems often mirror our distress at life's problems and recognising this can be the first step to recovery,' she says.

Andrew Honeyman examines the many addictions, among them alcohol, food, tranquillisers, other drugs, gambling and sex. He chronicles the mood swings, the changes in behaviour and personality, the self-hatred and negative feelings that go hand in hand with addiction. 'There is a point when a person emotionally, mentally, spiritually and physically breaks down under the stress and pain produced by an addiction,' he says.

Turning to the eating disorders we read that they are estimated to occur in one in five Irish women between the ages of fifteen and thirty. Two of the main disorders – anorexia (undereating to the point of starvation) and bulimia (compulsive binge eating) – are examined by Gillian Moore-Groarke. She argues that for an increasing number of women and for some men food has become something to be feared and, whenever possible, avoided.

Then there is sexual breakdown. Tom Kelly examines the most common sexual problems involving the quality and frequency of sexual intercourse. For men, there are erectile problems, the problems of premature ejaculation, retarded ejaculation, lack of interest in sex.

For women, there is vaginal spasm, inhibited sexual desire, difficulties with arousal and orgasm. This is one area, he says, where most couples are initially loath to involve a third party, with many struggling for years before turning to others for help.

OF THE MAJOR CAUSES of stress, bereavement ranks as one of the most significant and potentially destructive. Thérèse Brady describes the numbness, the sense of loss, the overriding despair, the hurt, guilt, blame, unresolved grief, desolation and loneliness. 'The knowledge of the inevitability of death does nothing to protect us from its devastating impact,' she concludes.

Eunice McCarthy turns to another source of loss, this time involving the loss of a job. Some of the emotions are similar to those of bereavement: the anger, hopelessness, despair. But there is also disillusionment, boredom, worthlessness, low self-esteem. 'Job loss introduces a new disorder into people's lives; feelings of security are disrupted and life becomes destabilised,' she says.

Work itself can also be stressful. Edward Hogan outlines the symptoms of occupational stress: reduced performance, decreased concentration, increased hostility, a sense of personal failure, culminating in exhaustion and burnout. There are many causes, he says, but an increasingly prominent factor is the growing uncertainty in the workplace, with its attendant threat of redundancy and job loss.

THE GROWING PRESSURES ON teenagers and young adults prompted me to include a chapter on adolescent stress. As Paul Andrews points out, one in five adolescents experiences appreciable psychological stress. And one in ten families experiences a dramatic deterioration of relationships between parents and teenage children.

Many of the adolescent moods, anxieties and other behaviour patterns may simply be a normal part of the struggle for identity and independence. Despite this, the topic should be addressed given the disturbing statistics and the trends in adolescent psychological problems.

The growing interest in post-traumatic stress also prompted an examination of this controversial disorder. 'No expert can predict which individuals will have to endure such chronic consequences,' says Fred Lowe. Among the consequences are recurring dreams, disturbing recollections, sudden flashbacks. 'One of the most common requests made by victims of trauma is to hope that their minds can be wiped clean ... they will never forget, but sensitive help and support will help them to live with their mental wounds,' he says.

ABOVE ALL, BOTH THIS book and the radio series offer practical advice. This is attempted in each paper, and two separate papers are devoted entirely to the task.

In 'Managing Stress Positively', Órla O'Neill examines the ways we can think, eat, exercise, relax, organise our way to managing stress. 'We can decide to behave in ways that help us to cope with stress, to become more effective managers of stressful situations,' she says.

'Coping with Pressure' is the theme of Aidan Moran's chapter. Drawing from the world of sport, he examines how we can prepare and control ourselves, focus our minds and our actions and adopt strategies to cope with the pressures of everyday life. 'Psychologically, the ability to *control* pressure is widely regarded as the key to winning,' he concludes.

THERE ARE MANY PEOPLE to be thanked for their help in getting this project off the ground. I am particularly grateful to Michael Littleton, John P Kelly, Tom Manning and Kevin Healy of RTE for their support and encouragement. My appreciation to John Spillane and Mary Feehan of Mercier Press for publishing the series. My thanks also to Danny McDonald of RTE for his help in compiling the radio programmes.

I am particularly indebted to the many case histories who selflessly and courageously told their stories on the radio broadcasts, yet who must remain anonymous. Most of all, I must mention the panel of experts who gave so generously of their time and their professional expertise. Finally, my thanks to Úna O'Hagan and Seán Keane for their patience over many long months. I hope the efforts of all have been worthwhile.

COLM KEANE

Nervous Breakdown

Anthony Clare

PSYCHIATRY, AS ITS CRITICS never tire to point out, is a jargon-infested area of discourse, full of mystifying terms such as libidinal cathexis, countertransference, bulimia, obsessive compulsive disorder, schizophrenia, conversion hysteria, borderline personality disorder. Lay terms are almost equally obfuscating – terms like 'nutter', 'loony', 'schizo', 'psycho'. These terms do little save dismiss, confuse, stigmatise and condemn. There is, however, one lay term which retains a potent, persistent appeal and which communicates powerfully, clearly and directly a potent truth about psychiatric illness. The term is 'nervous breakdown'.

'Nervous breakdown' covers all forms of mental illness and does not describe any nor discriminate between any. Many psychiatrists regard the term with the same distaste as cardiologists view the lay term 'heart attack' but nervous breakdown remains in robust and daily use. And it does this because, for all its looseness and vagueness and lack of precision, it embodies a fundamental truth about psychiatric ill-health, namely that at the core of all its various conditions and presentations is a *break down* in function, a seizing-up of the person, an insidious paralysis, in the case of depression, or wild going out of control, in the case of mania. Contained within the simple notion of breakdown are all the different elements that characterise the subjective experience of psychiatric ill-health – the loss of control, the feeling of helplessness, the sense of being unable to cope, the fear of disintegration, the apprehension that something terrible has happened or is about to happen.

IN SOME PSYCHIATRIC CONDITIONS the sense of impending or actual breakdown is *central* to the sufferer's experience. One such condition is so-called 'panic disorder'. Here is how

Marie, a woman in her early thirties, describes what she feels when such an attack occurs:

> I feel I am losing control and maybe even losing my mind. I was never a person like that. I could always control a lot of things. But because this was happening to me, I became very depressed in myself. I have never felt like this before. I had heard stories alright of people on the verge of nervous break-down. But that's how I felt at the time. I thought I was literally cracking up.

'Literally cracking up' – that is how so many people gripped by awesome apprehension, anxiety, fear actually feel. Some-times it is the 'fear' of breaking down which terrifies them – a sort of fear of fear. When asked what they think might happen if fear overwhelmed them in a shopping centre or church or lift or in an aircraft or wherever, such patients will invariably describe some terrible disintegration, some shud-dering to a stop, some descent into a kind of non-being – that they will seize up, that they will break down. People fear they may have a fit, may behave hysterically and embarrass-ingly, may lose consciousness, may make an exhibition of themselves, may even have a heart attack and die. Common to all such fears is the element of loss of control – that some-thing may happen over which the individual cannot exercise restraint.

The warning signs of psychiatric ill-health – disturbance of sleep, of concentration, of appetite, of drive, of zest, changes of mood, a terrible sense of panic, of being unable to cope – form the core of breakdown. There is the slow, insidi-ous, remorseless sense of impending disaster. But there is also this gnawing realisation of loss of control. Nowhere is this more evident than in clinical depression. Sufferers are stricken with a paralysis of feeling. The normal ability the healthy person has to lift a sadness or dampen excess excite-ment or elation is crucially impaired in disturbances of mood. And, despite everyone around one feeling and ap-pearing and sounding happy, the clinically depressed person remains flat, empty – 'broken down'. Listen to this account which captures so evocatively the absence of control at the heart of serious depression:

> I'll tell you this story. It was Christmas Day and I wasn't well, at all well. My husband had bought me a beautiful suit, a lovely ring, and I was sitting there, Christmas morning, and my neighbours and relations always came over, lovely time, the kids and all. And I was sitting at the dining-room table and they were all in the living-room. We had dividing doors. And there was a real pretence ... I had to pretend to be happy. And it was the awfullest thing I had to do in my life, because I wanted to be so happy. Everybody around me was happy that Christmas. And sitting in that chair I wished that all these people were gone and left me alone. It's so awful when you are that low. Words can't describe it. Well maybe somebody literate could describe it, but I could never describe that feeling. It was almost like you were on a desert island, all by yourself. But you could hear happy sounds, but you weren't even focussing in on those people. You were cut off in an isolated world. It was not nice.

WHAT THE TERM 'NERVOUS BREAKDOWN' neatly embodies is a key factor in the very definition of psychiatric illness – namely that what happens, what is experienced, is not under the person's control. The healthy person is in control – is an autonomous individual – and may choose to behave well or badly. Indeed, bad behaviour or deviance is distinguished from illness by this criterion – the sick person, in contrast to the bad person, is afflicted by impulses, feelings, sensations which do not appear to be under his or her immediate, personal control. In depression, in panic, in anxiety, in addiction, in crippling obsessional illness, in schizophrenia, the affected individual no longer controls or regulates his/her feelings, moods, even behaviours. The control has broken down.

This sense of cracking up, losing control, breaking down may be apparent to others but it may not be. Anne, a married woman in her mid-thirties, with three young children, suffers from panic attacks. They first started on a weekend break in the country. She describes the terrible sense of imminent disintegration she felt but those around her never suspected:

> I thought I was cracking up. I started to feel I was slipping at work. I wasn't coping as well in work as I had been. I always worked well under pressure and was hitting targets and that sort of thing. But it just wasn't happening for me. I felt I was slipping a lot with home life and the children and work. And there was a certain paranoia there because, although I felt I was slipping, it wasn't obvious to anyone else. When I would make a mistake I would say, 'Gosh, I'm losing it and I'm making more mistakes than I used to', and they'd say, 'No, you're doing fine'. And then I'd say, 'We're not going as many places as we had been going, because people were avoiding asking us because they knew there was a problem'. I was panicking. There was a certain madness there somewhere. And they were just avoiding asking us to functions and that sort of thing, and make a show of them or whatever. A grandmother of mine had pre-senile dementia and I was convinced that's where I was heading. I was getting it early, that was it. It was happening to me and I was just unfortunate.

Sometimes, there is the gnawing fear that other people *do* suspect, do know that all is not well, that the person concerned is 'breaking down'. Jacinta, a married woman in her thirties, who has had severe sexual problems since a car crash some years ago, expresses this anxiety most pointedly:

> I felt I had become a total lunatic. I felt as if the world saw me as the craziest person on earth. It was at a point where I was afraid of being out in front of people, people that I worked with, members of my family. I kept feeling that everybody else looked at me and saw me as this stranger ... 'she's not all together'. And that didn't do anything for me, from all the confused feelings I already had. And it was confirmation for me about how I felt about myself.

This account helps us understand why some people who feel they are cracking up begin to feel paranoid – that is to say, begin to feel an unrealistic sense that they are the centre of other people's attentions, interests, preoccupations. Jacinta feels bad, feels she is not coping, feels she is splitting apart. So intense and all-consuming are these feelings that they persuade her that other people, her family, her friends, her workmates, must notice that all is not well. They must be looking at her, thinking about her. Such feelings can insidiously grow. It is a short step indeed for Jacinta to begin to believe that people are talking about her, and another step to the conviction that perhaps they have something to do with how she feels, that maybe they mean harm or are trying to influence her in some particular way.

Of course often it *is* obvious to people – friends, relatives, spouses, siblings – that something is happening, that something is not quite right. However, almost invariably they believe that simple exhortation, encouragement, challenge will shake the affected person out of their panic, depression, apathy or fatigue. It is probably the most persistent and widespread misconception concerning psychiatric illness. Virtually every patient has experienced it and here is another describing how it feels:

> That is the worst thing anybody can turn around and say to you, you know, 'look, you should be down on your hands and knees thanking God. You have a lovely husband, two lovely children, a lovely home ... pull yourself together, cop on'. And you're sitting there in the depths of depression, so down. You actually feel that this person needs to go and get help, because they are right out of their mind, that anybody could even suggest these things to you and you feeling so, so down.

In June 1974, the Broadway producer, Joshua Logan, described his manic-depressive illness to a session of an American Psychiatric Association meeting in New York. Logan was one of the most talented producers of his time, having a string of hits, including the musical *South Pacific*, to his name. In the course of his address he had this to say about the 'come on and buck up' approach:

> It seemed to me that all friends of the average human being in depression only knew one cure-all, and that was a slap on the back and 'buck up'. It's just about the most futile thing that

21

could happen to you when you're depressed. My friends never even hinted to me that I was really ill. They simply thought that I was low and being particularly stubborn and difficult about things. If anyone had taken charge and insisted that I go to a mental hospital I probably would have gone straight off. Instead they simply said, 'Please don't act that way. Please don't look at your life so pessimistically; it's not so bad as you think. You'll always get back to it. Just buck up'.

Telling a depressed person to 'buck up' is about as useful as exhorting a seized car-engine to restart. That is the point of the notion of 'breakdown'. It makes plain the fact that, once it has occurred, the affected individual has passed a point of no return, beyond which he is no longer able on his/her own initiative to exercise control over his/her psychological life and functions. But breakdown, nervous breakdown, does not confine itself to psychological symptoms. People on the verge of a nervous breakdown, or deep within its throes, also frequently describe disturbing changes in physical experience too.

ONE OF THE REASONS that people in the throes of intense psychological strain and suffering believe that there is something *physical* wrong with them is that *physical* symptoms are often the most prominent of the symptoms they experience. Indeed, some of the earliest warning signs of a 'nervous breakdown' are physical – disturbances of sleep, fatigue, loss of appetite, loss of weight, palpitations (the rather frightening sensation of the heart beating rapidly inside the chest), abdominal discomfort (so-called 'butterflies'), tingling particularly of the hands and feet, sweating, nausea, diarrhoea, and, of course, pain. Many patients who are depressed, panicky, in considerable personal turmoil describe *pain*. The pain may be localised – in the stomach, in the head, in the chest. It may be instead a generally felt pain, difficult to locate but pain for all that. Indeed, it has been said by patients who have experienced both, that the pain of mental turmoil is worse and more unbearable than even the pain associated with a heart attack.

In 1982, Dr John Horder, a President of the Royal College of General Practitioners and a highly respected GP in North London, reflected in an interview on the relative agony he had experienced when, on separate occasions, he suffered from a heart attack and an episode of severe depression:

> If I had to choose again I would prefer to avoid the pain of depression. It is a surprisingly physical sensation, with a surprising resemblance to coronary pain because it too is total. But it cannot be relieved quickly. It even threatens life. It is oneself and not part of one's machinery – a form of total paralysis of desire, hope, capacity to decide, to do, to think or to feel – except pain and misery.

Some can feel so bad they begin to worry whether they will even survive. Sarah, a married woman in her thirties, who has suffered from chronic sleep disturbances for over ten years, gives a fairly classic description of this fear:

> It's like as if somebody has two needles at the end of your feet and they're just pulling the blood right out of you. You just feel drained totally and very cold. There were many days I thought I was actually dying. I used to feel so tired that I either thought I had some dreadful disease that was incurable that they couldn't find or that I was dying and nobody knew I was dying.

The 'pain' that those who have had depression often describe is one of the reasons that some sufferers are driven to self-destruction. But there are other, related reasons. Many depressed individuals become convinced that they constitute such a burden to those who are closest to them that all concerned would be better off if they ended their lives. In a few tragic, but much-reported cases, the depressed individual, unable to see anything in life other than pain, loss, destruction or corruption, concludes that not merely he but his loved ones would be better off if he were dead. Tom, a sufferer from depression, talks about such feelings:

> I felt that if I ended it all, I wasn't ending it for myself. I was ending the pain and suffering for my children and my wife.

23

And I was going to make life easier for them by being gone, because they hadn't got the responsibility for me then anymore. I was gone and out of their lives, so they could get on with living their own lives instead of worrying about me. I didn't want them to have to shoulder that, because I felt I was going mad and I didn't want them to have to live with that.

In coping with the pressure and pain of breakdown, some people paradoxically end up inflicting pain on themselves. In part, this self-destruction is a measure of the corrosive loss of confidence and self-esteem that is a feature of virtually all psychological distress. In part, it is a crucial and central feature of a number of particular disorders such as the eating disorders, anorexia and bulimia nervosa. Here is how one sufferer, Joan, describes the confused feelings of someone prepared to inflict considerable suffering on herself to avoid what she perceives to be the even worse prospect – namely, being overweight:

> I can remember sitting on the bathroom floor and I was very ill. I had made myself sick, but I was ill as well, felt weak. And I just lay there on the floor, couldn't move. And I thought, 'What are you doing to yourself? Is it going to be like this for the rest of your life? Are you going to be ever satisfied with your weight?' And I felt like the walls were crowding in around me, things were getting really bad.

MANY PEOPLE, EXPERIENCING SOME of these psychological and physical symptoms and fearing that they may be 'breaking down', attempt to cope, to stay in control by a fierce act of will or by resorting to one or more of a variety of stratagems. The businessman who teeters on the edge of falling apart may bolster his nerves, or try to cure his insomnia, with alcohol. The housebound housewife, overwhelmed by panic and fear of going mad, may resort to tranquillisers. The student, desperately trying to gain control of a syllabus which seems at every glance to be enormous and growing, may struggle to stay afloat and in control by the use of stimulants such as caffeine and amphetamines. The compulsive eater asserts a degree of control over her weight by adopting the strategy of following every eating binge with an episode of self-induced vomiting. Many attempt to silence the sounds of stress and strain by immersing themselves in desperate action, a relentless rushing about and doing; others struggle to cope by withdrawing ever further into themselves. And then again there is simple denial – the depressive slipping slowly into despair, the manic sensing that the surge of energy euphoria is not under control, the alcoholic falling prey to the drink he had hitherto forsworn, all may adopt the despairing remedy of insisting in the face of obvious disaster that all is well.

The problem with these and similar attempts to stay in charge is that they actually aggravate the breakdown. Yet for a while, for a brief period of illusion, they can provide a sense of security. Joan, addicted to alcohol, pills and slimming, and who has battled with these addictions for over twenty years, explains:

> You feel you are just held together by the booze and the pills. You feel that if you don't take them you're going to splinter and break and there's going to be nothing there. So they're kind of gelling you together. But you want to give them up, and you are so afraid because, if you give them up, what will you have because you are nothing else? So you feel you are just going to collapse and break down, collapse in a heap. It's not a nice feeling.

The sense of breaking down is not a nice feeling. It is, however, a warning feeling. Just as the physical organism, pushed to the limit of its endurance, will manifest warning signs – breath gasping, limbs aching, heart pumping rapidly – so psychological strain has its warning signs – irritability, sleep disturbance, loss of zest, feelings of panic, marked apprehension. These symptoms – the harbingers of breakdown – deserve to be taken seriously. Ignoring them carries much the same dangers as ignoring physical pain, physical fatigue, physical exhaustion.

Further Reading
Sutherland, Stuart, *Breakdown*, Weidenfeld and Nicholson, London,

1987.

Goldbery, David and Huxley, Peter, *Common Mental Disorders*, Routledge, London, 1992.

Kuipers, Liz and Bebbington, Paul, *Living with Mental Illness*, Condor/Souvenir Press, London, 1987.

Gibbs, Angelina, *Understanding Mental Health*, The Consumers' Association/Hodder and Stoughton, London, 1986.

Milligan, Spike and Clare, Anthony, *Depression and How to Survive It*, Ebury Press, London, 1993.

Howe, Gwen, *The Reality of Schizophrenia*, Faber and Faber, London, 1990.

Storr, Anthony, *The Integrity of the Personality*, Oxford University Press, Oxford, 1992.

DEPRESSION

Anthony Bates

THERE ARE TIMES WHEN anyone can say 'I have had enough, I simply can't take anymore'. A variety of pressures seem to bear down on us, leaving us tired, drained, with nothing more to give. The most difficult stresses are those involving personal loss or potential loss, e.g. loss of a job, loss of mobility, breakdown of a close relationship. Other significant stresses are those that undermine that basic feeling of control we need to have over our lives, e.g. family, social and financial pressures. Yet, somehow we do cope, most of the time. What helps is that some key elements in our lives remain in place; that we maintain some degree of faith in ourselves, and find compassion and intelligent support from others.

For some people, however, life can be specially painful. Personal crises of the kind mentioned above can trigger reactions that are intense and disabling. Perhaps it is the effect of too many stresses over a long time, perhaps they lack support; perhaps it is that a crisis touches at the heart of a deeply personal insecurity, stirring up massive self-doubt; or perhaps it is some weakness in their constitution that makes it hard to cope with stress. Whatever the particular configuration of factors may be, the end result for some is an inward collapsing of their self-esteem, a paralysis of their ability to cope, and a gradual withdrawal into personal despair that attempts to shut out the world. This form of human suffering, this kind of breakdown, we call depression.

The term 'depression', as used in a medical or therapeutic context, denotes something different to simply 'feeling depressed' from time to time. A person who is feeling depressed about something can generally experience a lifting of their spirits when given appropriate support and reassurance by friends, or when outside pressures are removed.

Someone who experiences clinical depression experiences a condition which is more painful and does not seem to respond to the concern and comfort of others.

Depression is characterised by a particular set of changes in the way a person thinks, feels, and behaves. A depressed individual's thinking is characterised by extreme self-criticism, pessimism, hopelessness about the future, a profound conviction that they are in some way a failure as a human being. For depressed people important achievements in their past no longer seem to count as they focus exclusively on every sign of failure or weakness that they can possibly point to in their life. These preoccupations seriously reduce their ability to concentrate – a very depressed person may find it hard to read more than a paragraph of a newspaper or book. Such is their loss of confidence that even the simplest decisions they are faced with can prove to be an enormous strain: they cannot trust themselves to do the right thing.

To the depressed person there is very little in life that gives pleasure. Activities that previously were important to them no longer hold their interest. Sadness or gloom may permeate their conversation, although this can often be masked behind complaints of feeling 'very unwell'. It is quite likely that a very depressed person might describe feeling tired, drained or irritable, rather than come straight out and say they feel sad and helpless.

Depression is, for many people, a very physical experience and the feelings they describe are often to do with changes they experience in their body. They may describe the sensation of hurting deeply inside somewhere, they may report weight loss due to a complete loss of appetite for food. They may find themselves unable to make love and indeed have very little interest in doing so, which can be a major worry for them. Sleep may be disturbed and they may have vague physical complaints which cause them to seek numerous medical consultations before the real problem is identified.

A significant slowing down in activity is a very common feature of depression, although some sufferers can become restless, even hyperactive, as they try to block out the sense of torment they experience inside. One man, who was in his mid-thirties, described how his 'get-up-and-go' was all gone. There is little energy to devote to external demands and concerns. A tendency to take to the bed is all too common. The experience of depression makes one feel very isolated, whether or not there are others around, and sometimes it can seem easier just to retreat into one's own company to avoid having to deal with the criticism, demands, even concerns, of loved ones and friends.

Depression may be experienced to a mild, moderate or severe degree. In its mild or moderate forms, it is characterised by negative thinking and low self-esteem, irritability, difficulty concentrating, and a general loss of interest in the world around. In the more severe forms of depression the same symptoms are experienced with greater intensity and there are also physical manifestations of this mental torment. Symptoms of fatigue, insomnia or hypersomnia (too little or too much sleep), decreased appetite and weight loss and a marked slowing down of physical and mental activity indicate the need for specialised help. Suicidal thoughts often lurk just beneath the surface and should always be checked for and regarded with the utmost seriousness. A diagnosis of severe or 'major' depression is applicable if the majority of these symptoms are experienced every day for at least *two weeks*.

ESTIMATES SUGGEST THAT BETWEEN 8 and 10 people out of every 100, which means approximately 300,000 people in Ireland, are acutely depressed. Most of these depressions occur in individuals aged between 25 and 65 years, with the incidence increasing with age. Estimates for the over 65 age group are that between 10% and 17% are significantly depressed at any one time. In spite of its frequency – depression has been called the *common cold of psychiatry* – only 10% of the people who become depressed seek help professionally, often due to a feeling of shame about what they regard as a flaw in their character.

Though the great majority of cases occur in adults, depression may occur at any time from early childhood to old age. One study of 3,000 school children found that 5.2% of the group were reporting mild to moderate depression. Chronic marital conflict, parental rejection, or serious stresses in adjusting to school often account for such reactions. Sadness, anxiety and fearfulness may reflect childhood depression, but the picture is occasionally dominated by poor schoolwork or aggressive behaviour which may mislead parents into misinterpreting the nature of the problem.

One remarkably consistent finding in studies across different continents has been that women are about twice as likely to experience depression as men. The greatest number of depressed women are in the 20–40 age group, and in those who are at home caring for young children. Men and women become depressed in equal numbers where they are in similar roles such as in student life or in a high status career group. Whether or not women's biological constitution renders them more likely to become depressed than men has been hotly debated. The weight of evidence would seem to be that women are no more vulnerable to depression than men provided they are not dealing with added stresses of home and family coupled with isolation and lack of support.

In adults and children alike depression can go unnoticed for long periods as they express the problem in unexpected ways. For example, an adolescent may begin to act in an uncharacteristic way, participating in shop-lifting, fire-setting or disruptive behaviour at school. An adult may come forward with a problem of sexual impotence, severe procrastination, or vague physical complaints for which there is no apparent cause. Often adults abuse alcohol to kill the pain, which makes them feel worse in the long-run, and compounds their basic sense of inadequacy.

THIS CHAPTER IS AN ATTEMPT to spell out the message that depression is best understood as an end-product of stress impacting on specific vulnerabilities in an individual's personality, constitution and social circumstances. Personality, social, and biological vulnerabilities can render a person prone to depression and these are discussed separately now.

Personality factors: perhaps the most striking characteristic of depression-prone individuals is their belief that there is something fundamentally bad or incompetent about them as human beings. This is often referred to as having a poor self-image. The image we have of ourselves is principally formed through the feedback we receive from those most closely involved in our rearing. An unresponsive parent, or a constantly critical or abusive parent will eventually create within the child a sense that they are not adequate or loved. Traumas, such as the loss of a parent, severe illness and hospitalisation can undermine a child's sense of security. Similar experiences in adult life, or the threat of loss or abandonment by a loved one, can awaken painful memories which they have never resolved.

Research supports the role of negative early experience in depression and has found that the majority of patients hospitalised for severe depression have experienced some major loss in the first five years. Loss of a parent in children under eleven leaves them especially vulnerable to attacks of depression in adult circumstances where they are without support. Clinical experience suggests that the self-loathing and self-criticism so common in depression sufferers more often reflect the attitude taken toward them as children.

When childhood experience leaves you feeling very insecure, survival demands that you work out strategies for covering your insecurities and 'proving' your worth as a human being. For example, those who were hurt by an unresponsive or harshly critical parent may devote a lot of energy to making sure they are liked and approved by others and avoiding conflict if at all possible. They live by the rule that says 'to feel good about myself, I must make sure I'm liked by other people' or 'always put the needs of others first'. Others whose early experience left them not only with self-doubts but a severe lack of trust in others, may build their self-esteem exclusively on the merits of their achievement and success. Their rule of living becomes 'to feel good about myself, I must perform perfectly and always be on top of things'.

While both of these strategies are attempts to maintain a

high level of self-esteem they can leave a person very vulnerable to depression. To build one's self-confidence on the shifting sands of people's approval is clearly a very dubious and dangerous venture. Equally, to demand perfection of oneself constantly, is a fairly sure guarantee that one will react very badly to failure.

Social factors: there are factors that can directly undermine a person's self-esteem that have to do with their current social situation. Poor housing, social isolation and the pressures of rearing young children with no support – especially more than three young children – increase vulnerability to depression. One interesting piece of research which highlights the crucial role of social support in staying mentally well, is the finding that women in stressful social circumstances with even one close, confiding friend, were four times less likely to become depressed than those women in similar circumstances who did not have such a friendship.

Unemployment clearly has an impact on an individual's self-esteem and where there is any vulnerability to depression it undoubtedly aggravates it. Research has found that being employed decreases one's chance of becoming depressed by a factor of ten; in other words, individuals in difficult social situations are ten times more likely to be depressed if they are without employment than if they have steady employment.

Many different forms of social injustice exist that can erode an individual's sense of dignity and the experience of repeatedly trying, in vain, to change a bad situation can eventually produce in them a condition psychologists call 'learned helplessness' – the belief that nothing you do matters since control over your life is totally in the hands of others. People in such situations find stresses gradually building up which never seem to get resolved until something finally happens that is simply 'the last straw', which breaks their spirit and throws them into depression.

Biological Factors: there are differences in people's physical capacity to absorb stress, depending on their genetic constitution, which appear to leave some individuals prone to mood swings. Specific biological vulnerabilities have been suggested to explain those recurrent depressions that have a striking physical component. In these conditions, movement and speech can be slow and patients can wake early and feel unable to face the day, but find their mood seems to lift as the day goes on.

This biological explanation of depression postulates that there are specific biochemical changes in the brain that affect particular nerve pathways. The pathways affected are thought to be those controlled by the chemicals noradrenalin and serotonin. Serotonin is a chemical which, when released in the brain, regulates mental arousal. In severe episodes of depression there is a malfunction in the amount of serotonin available which in turn may contribute to the fatigue, listlessness and sleep disturbance so characteristic of depression.

Episodes of depression are particularly deemed to be 'biological' when they occur in someone who has a diagnosis of manic depression, a condition which produces a mood disorder with varying episodes of mania, characterised by a variety of symptoms including inappropriate elation, extreme motor activity, impulsiveness, an excessively rapid pattern of speech, and severe episodes of depression, as described above.

RECOVERY FROM DEPRESSION BEGINS when sufferers reach the point of accepting that they are trapped in a prison and need help. While they may want the pain to go away, a part of them may also want to remain within the security of their prison because they are convinced they cannot cope with whatever pressures exist outside. Drugs may lift their mood but at some point sufferers must choose to confront the pain of their life, both past or present. Recovery can mean finally grieving a real event in their lives that has been painful and that can never be fixed. It may also mean changing long-standing habits of negative thinking and trying new ways of dealing with difficult situations. For many, a relationship with a competent therapist who can guide them in their journey may be vital. Therapy helps people find doors in the walls that surround them.

As a therapist, meeting someone for the first time in deep depression, I am struck by how confused and demoralised they are by the experience. My first concern is to be available to them in their pain, to hear them out as they describe what has often been a lonely hell, and restore a feeling of hope that their pain will end. By listening carefully to their story I help them make sense of why they feel depressed and dispel the fear that they're 'going mad'. Instead of viewing their condition as a never-ending affliction they begin to see it as the result of a number of specific, understandable problems that can be resolved.

Depressed patients are usually confronted with multiple pressures which need to be eased to make recovery possible. In reviewing their current life-situation we look at practical ways of removing stress. Often, very simple actions on their part can make a difference. Postponing certain duties that do not require immediate attention, cancelling unimportant events, arranging to take a weekend off, finding out exactly where they stand in relation to some matter so they can stop worrying about it, or asking help of friends, can help greatly ease their situation.

Medication is always an option I discuss with someone who is severely depressed. People often hold strong feelings against taking drugs. Such a move can seem like giving in and committing themselves to a life of dependency. They often have past experiences of being offered drugs that didn't help or were prescribed without any attempt to get to the root of their problems. As a psychologist I cannot prescribe medications but I am fortunate to work with good psychiatrists who can offer this option in a sensitive and intelligent manner if it is indicated. While I am personally committed to helping depressed individuals without drugs, I believe they offer certain people huge relief and the combination of medication and therapy enables a much faster recovery. This is particularly true where there is an intense experience of pain, a family history of depression, or when the sufferer reports serious suicidal feelings.

Early interventions in therapy for depression aim to reduce fear, restore hope, and relieve stress where possible. I also look for simple ways that sufferers can take control of their life-situation. For example, procrastination afflicts many depressed individuals. They avoid tasks that require attention because they believe it will be 'too much' or 'too upsetting'. Together we identify one such task and break it down into 'bite-size' steps which they complete between therapy sessions. We take time to plan how they execute this 'homework' and make sure to think through how they will handle obstacles that may crop up. Nothing succeeds like success – the smallest victory, having had the bitter taste of failure for so long, helps restore self-confidence, lift the mood, and put the lie to the belief 'I'm inadequate'. Whenever sufferers realise that they can make a difference to their mood, that they can change the way they feel, they are encouraged to gradually exercise control over other aspects of their life.

The therapy I practice is called cognitive therapy. The word *cognitive* simply means *the way we look at things*. This approach believes that the way we think about ourselves and the world is critical in making us prone to depression. A healthy and happy acceptance of oneself – a positive self-image – is the best protection against depression. Cognitive therapy believes that people remain vulnerable to depression because of the negative attitude they hold towards themselves and the rigid rules of living they have carried over from childhood. Those prone to depression still believe they are not quite OK, and try to earn self-worth by demanding of themselves that they constantly 'take care of others', or 'be number one in everything they do' or 'keep secret all their weaknesses because if others find out they will despise them', etc. For me the heart of therapy has to do with helping someone to see how their particular beliefs may be keeping them depressed, and showing them how it is possible to live without constantly nagging oneself to be 'perfect', 'reasonable', 'caring', 'approved of', every waking moment!

Depression may be a painful crisis but it can also be an opportunity to challenge and dissolve rigid beliefs that have cramped our lives, denied our humanity, and limited our capacity to be close to others. Therapy helps identify and dispel those self-defeating ideas that no longer serve us, even if they once seemed to be the only way of looking at things. The goal should not only be to feel better, but to recover a true image of ourselves, to find the courage to face life, and to enjoy the wonder and craziness of it all with those we love.

Further Reading

Rowe, Dorothy, *Depression – The way out of your prison*, Routledge, London, 1983.

Burns, David D., *Feeling Good – The New Mood Therapy*, New American Library, New York, 1980.

Barker, Philip J., *A Self-Help Guide to Managing Depression*, Chapman and Hall, London and New York, 1993.

Milligan, Spike and Clare, Anthony, *Depression and How to Survive It*, Ebury Press, London, 1993.

McKeon, Patrick, *Coping with Depression and Elation*, Sheldon Press, London, 1986.

Bates, Anthony, 'Cognitive-Behavioural Therapy,' in *Psychotherapy in Ireland*, edited by Edward Boyne, Columba, Dublin, 1993.

SLEEP PROBLEMS

MARIE MURRAY

Lying awake, calculating the future,
Trying to unweave, unwind, unravel
And piece together the past and the future,
Between midnight and dawn, when the past is all deception,
The future futureless.

T. S. ELIOT – *The Dry Salvages*

THERE IS NO GREATER indication that 'something' is wrong than when our sleep breaks down. This chapter explores our understanding of sleep and sleeplessness and the conditions and circumstances in which sleep may be disturbed. We will examine the experience of sufferers of sleep disturbance and suggest strategies to help if sleep is a problem for you.

Our lives are punctuated by sleep. It is estimated that we spend about one-third of our time in sleep, yet it is a state which we still do not entirely understand and about which we have great curiosity. There is something intensely fascinating about that mysterious time in which we dream. In history, culture and literature, there are myriad myths, fears, beliefs and portents which surround our dreams.

Sleep is important in our lives. We devote special times, a special room, furniture and clothes to it. People who suffer sleep disturbance and deprivation experience an overwhelming drive to sleep. Those who nightly cannot sleep, describe the misery of the night hours. Then, it seems, they alone are tossing and turning, or pacing around a silent darkened house, ravaged in pursuit of the ease and nourishment of sleep.

The fear of not sleeping causes sleeplessness for many people. Counting sheep is more likely to give you a headache than lull you into a restful doze. Notions of 'early to bed, early to rise' as the only possible pattern for health, wealth and wisdom serve to add to tensions about sleep. Many people survive well on a little sleep and are still ener-

37

getic and eager into the night hours. Others become comatosed by evening and feel positively deprived if they sleep less than 9 hours. What we need is what we need personally to function well the next day. There is no doubt that 'sleep knits up the ravell'd sleeve of care' and there is nothing nicer than to cosy down into our nests at the end of a bad day. If sleep eludes us and we are continually ragged-edged, then we have a problem. What we need to explore is whether this is primarily a sleep problem or a symptom of other ills.

SLEEP HAS BEEN DESCRIBED as a normal state, in which there is decreased mobility and less efficient responsiveness to the outside world. While we sleep, the rational thinking part of our brain is not active and there is a slowing down of other bodily functions. But the brain is still active in certain ways. It filters important sounds (e.g., a mother will hear a child crying) and it responds to bodily states such as cold and hunger. Sleep occurs on a regulated basis and is contrasted with wakefulness, which is a time of increased and efficient response.

Sleep centres in the brain control our pattern of sleep and arousal. We have biological cycles that repeat approximately every 24 hours known as 'circadian rhythms'. We have many such rhythms regulating, for example, sleep/arousal, rest/activity, hunger/eating, hormonal balance and body temperature. Our ability to sleep is connected to those cycles.

In the past, our biological rhythms were much more harmonious with nature. They were in tune with the seasons, with the dark and cold for sleep, and the sun and warmth for activity. It is harder for children to sleep in summer 'daylight' and harder for us to get up to dark Irish winter mornings. With technological change has also come biological disruption. Heating, lighting, shift work, jet lag and 'stress of modern living' have all contributed towards a disruption of this natural rhythm.

The rhythm of body temperature shows that it is highest in the middle of the day and lowest in the middle of the night. If you have spent a night travelling or working, you will experience this temperature change even if you have prepared by sleeping the previous day. There is a struggle to stay alert and awake throughout the night. By morning, there is often a second 'awakening' with increased energy and alertness, although you have been up longer and should be even more exhausted. This is a prime example of the circadian rhythm. Disruption of sleep can also cause disruption of hormonal balance. Stress and anxiety cause the release of increased adrenalin (hormone released in flight/fright and situations of threat). The anxiety engendered by fear of not sleeping can thereby perpetuate difficulty in getting to sleep.

THE BRAIN PRODUCES ELECTRICAL activity (brain waves) which can be measured on a machine called an electroencephalogram or EEG. The patterns of this activity change between sleep and wakefulness. A revolution in sleep research occurred in 1953 when Eugene Aserinsky and Nathaniel Kleitman described sleep in relation to the electrical activity they recorded when they observed rapid eye movements in sleeping people. The sleep cycle was found to consist of two distinct stages and four sub-stages. These were defined by the appearance of particular wave patterns on the EEG. It takes about 90 minutes to pass through the complete sequence of sleep stages and this is repeated several times each night.

There are two, now well-known, distinct stages of sleep:
1) Rapid eye movement, REM, or paradoxical sleep.
2) Non-rapid eye movement, NREM, or orthodox sleep which is further divided into four sub-stages, which will be discussed later.

Researchers began waking up subjects when they noted rapid eye movements and found that most people (over 80%) who were woken at this time described dreams. REM sleep became associated with the time when dreaming most occurs and the more 'active' the dream, the more rapid the eye movements. REM sleep is associated with increased brain blood flow and is the time during which brain regeneration takes place. Non-rapid eye movement (NREM) may be related to bodily restitution. The skin is revitalised by the growth of new cells and we produce more of them during sleep. Loss of sleep leads to visible effects in the skin, so when we talk about getting our 'beauty sleep' we are referring to a physiological fact! In short, REM is brain repair and NREM bodily repair.

When we go to bed our brain activity shows a normal waking pattern. We then drift into sleep, our muscles relax and the brain settles into a steady rhythm. We divide this sleeping process, or slow wave sleep, or NREM sleep, into four stages:

1) We move from a restful transitional state into Stage 1 sleep which is akin to dozing.
2) Stage 2 is deeper and has even slower brain waves.
3) These get progressively larger and slower in Stages 3 and 4.
4) Stage 4 is a stage of deep restorative quiet sleep which we associate with a good night's sleep.

It is progressively more difficult to wake a sleeper as these stages progress from 1 to 4. The longest and deepest period of slow-wave sleep each night is the first period of Stage 3 and 4. This occurs usually within about two hours of falling asleep. In 'normal' sleep, REM only occurs after the deeper stages of sleep (Stages 2–4). Those woken during REM sleep recall vivid and colourful imagery and dreams. People who are awoken more than 10 minutes after REM sleep has ended tend not to report such dreams. It is in this way that we have come to understand the patterns of sleep and dreaming. Sleep walking and night terrors tend to happen in the early stages of sleep (NREM) and are usually never remembered.

SLEEP DEPRIVATION STUDIES SHOW the importance of sleep. Films of war or espionage highlight the use of sleep-deprivation or 'brain-washing' to confuse and disorientate. People become frantic and lose their sense of reality. One imagines the white light shining in the exhausted victim's eyes as he pleads for sleep. There are interesting studies showing the effects of deprivation at the different stages. If volunteers are deprived of REM sleep, memory and skills are often affected. If deprived of Stage 4 sleep, people feel extremely tired and apathetic. One of the problems associated with sleeping tablets is that they are reported to reduce the proportion of REM sleep in relation to NREM – a sleeping tablet and a normal sleep are completely different.

HOW MUCH SLEEP DOES a person need? If you struggle bleary-eyed and cranky from your bed, the typical morning grouch, then you have probably not had enough sleep! There is great variability in sleep requirements and total sleep time. It is said that, for adults, anything between 6 and 9 hours sleep as a nightly average is not unusual and $7^{1}/2$ hours is a norm. Those who complain that they 'never slept a wink all night' have often slept much more than they think. It is, therefore, not just time but quality of sleep that affects us.

It is estimated that 66% of people sleep between $6^{1}/2$ and $8^{1}/2$ hours on a regular basis. There are those who seem to have a lesser sleep requirement. Several important characters in history have been accredited with very short sleeping times. Writers, artists, scientists, politicians, innovators have been associated with lesser sleeping hours. One of the major complaints of parents of gifted children is that they sleep very little. They want to be up and doing, exploring and learning. Many people have 'trained' themselves to reclaim those night hours. These are the night owls who refuse to bed down and lose precious night time. Creativity is sometimes associated with the quiet of the night. Others prefer to sleep awhile and meet the dawn with creativity. It is estimated that 18% of people sleep for less than $6^{1}/2$ hours and 16% sleep for more than $8^{1}/2$ hours. It is particularly interesting that people who regularly sleep only 3 hours per night get greater amounts of REM and Stage 4 (restorative sleep) than those who sleep on an 8 hour schedule get in their first 3 hours. They actually manage to maintain the usual amount of non-REM sleep. When people are sleep-deprived, on subsequent 'recovery nights' there is an increase in REM to compensate.

People express increased anxiety about sleep and their

sleeping patterns. There is a preoccupation with too little or too much sleep. They worry that it is too light, too deep, too dream-laden or dream-free. This concern has heightened the problem for those who suffer a change in sleeping pattern so that one might say 'the problem becomes the problem'. The fear of sleeplessness causes sleeplessness and the demands of the day ahead can seem alarming without 'a good night's sleep' to help. It may be comforting to know that sleep deprivation studies, for the most part, show good recovery in the sleep-deprived. There is the famous case of a 17 year-old volunteer who undertook 264 hours without sleep. He was noted during that time to have irritability, blurred vision, slurring of speech, memory lapses and some confusion about his identity. No long-term effects were found on his personality or his intellect and his first recovery sleep session was less than 15 hours. His sleep showed increases in Stage 4 NREM and REM sleep. Although Freud saw the dream as the safety valve to release emotional tension, REM sleep deprivation studies do not show psychological disruption. There have been some studies that have even suggested that REM sleep deprivation may be helpful in treating depression.

Age has been consistently related to the differing amount and quality and patterning of sleep. Newborn infants may spend an average of 16 hours in sleep. There may be five to six periods of sleep per day. This drops during the first year. At 2–3 years the range is 9–12 hours. Amongst the elderly there may be a partial return to a sleep pattern of infancy and childhood with more daytime naps. It is said that the elderly need more rest and less sleep. Apart from age factors, the effect of loss of sleep on a person is heightened by the demands made of them on the following day. There are differing requirements and responsibilities at different life stages: childhood, adolescence, adulthood, later years.

SLEEP DISORDERS AND DISTURBANCES: It is not possible, nor intended, in this chapter, to examine sleep disorders in depth. I will, however, attempt a brief description of some of the main disorders.

Primary disturbances of the sleep–wakefulness mechanisms were dramatically outlined in the film 'Awakenings' with Robin Williams, about the encephalitis lethargica epidemic which was known as 'sleeping sickness'. Narcolepsy involves irresistible brief episodes of sleep. Hypersomnia refers to sleep attacks of less urgency but lasting longer. It is also seen in Kleine–Levine Syndrome where the attack can last up to 20 hours and may occur several times a year. Medical disorders include Sleep Apnoea (from the Greek word for 'breathlessness'). This is a condition that includes noisy strenorous snoring with cessation of breathing or upper air-way blockage. A recent medical report from the two sleep disorder laboratories at St Vincent's Public and Private Hospitals in Dublin indicates that they are now assessing twice the number of patients than a year ago. Additionally, there are sleep symptoms of the major psychiatric disorders and sleep is altered in major depression. The symptomatology of many illnesses and syndromes includes sleep problems. Sleep is also altered when we are excited, upset, stressed or have a big event the next day.

INSOMNIA IS ONE OF the most common complaints in general medical practice and is estimated to occur in approximately 30% of the normal population. In clinical practice, psychologists and psychotherapists regularly find that the initial presenting complaint is a sleep problem – therapy often reveals other psychological hurts and distresses.

People who complain of insomnia may report difficulty in falling asleep (Initial Insomnia). Sometimes people experience waking up in the middle of the night and having great difficulty going back to sleep (Middle Insomnia). The more serious insomnia and the type most associated with depression is awakening early without being able to sleep again (Terminal Insomnia). This is one of the essential elements in a diagnosis of clinical depression and is often referred to as Early Morning Waking or EMW.

In sleep, people may have episodes of sleep-talking (somniloquy), sleep-walking (somnambulism), bed-wetting (enuresis) and tooth-grinding (bruxism) and snoring. Snoring occurs in 20% of men and 5% of women under 35. By our sixties this has increased to 60% of men and 40% of women. Partners of snorers can have very disturbed sleep, giving rise to the joke 'snore and you sleep alone'. Sleep-walking is much more common in children and occurs in only about 2% of adults. Night terrors (parvor nocturnus) are also associated with childhood. The child may scream and sit up in apparent terror which is inconsolable. This is usually not remembered.

Nightmares are frightening experiences in sleep and exploration of the meaning of these can be cues to a person's distress. People who have had accidents, losses, car crashes or traumas often report nightmares. In therapy, exploring the nightmare can cue us to present and past traumas in a person's life.

WHAT CAUSES OUR SLEEP pattern to break down? Apart from the primary disturbances and medical factors outlined, the 'causes' are, perhaps, as many as the individuals who suffer. Sleep problems are symptomatic of many levels of distress. Those of us who work as therapists are aware, when we first meet clients, that it may be some time before the 'origin' of the problem unfolds. The following are some of the more commonly presenting causes.

Bereavement: during the time when a family member is seriously ill, the care of that person may involve many sleepless or sleep-broken nights attending to them. This throws the biological clock and sleep pattern awry. People experience stress and concern and anticipation of loss. When death comes, the partner, left alone, often finds the grief and mourning unbearable. At a time when they need sleep most, the 'balm of hurt minds', it eludes them. The mourning process involves anger (why me?), guilt (did I do enough?) and fear (will I cope alone?) and inevitable sleeplessness. The night can be very long and lonely, filled with sadness and regret and longing.

Stress: chronic or ongoing stress can be much more harmful than an acute reaction to a specific situation. When primitive man encountered a danger, such as a lion, his body became mobilised for 'fight or flight'. This physiological reaction was useful for survival and is still useful in situations of extreme danger. When the danger passes, the body relaxes. Today, there are many people who live out their lives in that state of mobilisation or stress. They suffer from relentless ongoing hurry and stress; the missing car keys, the traffic jam, the deadlines, the struggle to compete and achieve. Type A personalities, who are ambitious, impatient, competitive, were identified by heart specialists, Friedman and Rosenman, as coronary-prone individuals. These people are most likely to suffer many symptoms: headaches, backache, palpitations, nausea, tiredness and sleeplessness. One of the most prominent signals of stress is sleeplessness. The body and mind become too tense and alert to go into the relaxation required for sleep. For these people, the cause of their sleep problem is relatively clear, i.e., their approach to life and lifestyle. The 'cure' is equally clear: change in beliefs and values (cognitive reappraisal), change in lifestyle and training in relaxation.

Depression: depression is one of the most common medical disorders. It can occur at any age and with primary symptoms that do not involve obvious mood change. It would not be possible to go into the subcategories of depression in this chapter. Disturbance of sleep is often a signal that a person may be depressed. Depression includes irritability, loss of interest and pleasure in life, weight loss or gain, fatigue or loss of energy. People often report feelings of worthlessness or guilt. They complain of poor concentration or impaired ability to make decisions. They may be preoccupied with thoughts of death. Life can seem hopeless if you are depressed. It is important in these instances to recognise sleep as a symptom and seek help.

Pain: pain can keep you awake. Pain-killers may be effective for a number of hours but as the affects wear off, the person is aroused from sleep. Back-sufferers particularly complain of sleep problems. It is difficult to get comfortable and if changing posture in sleep causes pain, we awake. The sleep pattern is disrupted with chronic pain and this can lead to depression.

Any illness can disrupt the sleep pattern, such as a cold, a tickly cough, asthma, toothache, headache, hay fever. Some medical symptoms, such as attacks of angina, duodenal ulcers or epileptic discharge, are increased during sleep.

Relationship Problems: conflict between marital partners produces much distress for the couple themselves and for their children. It is difficult to share a bed and sleep beside someone with whom you are angry. The physiological arousal of anger defies sleep.

Children who are stressed or upset by the tension at home will often express their distress at night. Their anxiety affects their sleep, disrupting parents' sleep and leading to further family tension.

Teenagers asserting their independence through late nights or loud music or late television viewing can alter the family's sleep routine. Parents worry for their children's safety when they are out. Collecting children from discos and parties may keep parents up later at night.

Tracking the origin of sleep problems often reveals relationship problems which are addressed best through marital or family therapy.

Psychological Problems: the experience of living brings with it the gamut of joy and sorrow, of 'agony and ecstasy'. At night, tormenting thoughts of the day's worries often crowd in. Financial worries, job concerns, family stresses, loss and anticipated loss often seem more acute at night. Sleep problems often mirror our distress at life's problems and recognising this can be the first step to recovery.

OVERCOMING SLEEP PROBLEMS: THE first task is to uncover the root of the problem. Whatever its cause, there is usually a solution. The following are suggestions for breaking the debilitating cycle of sleep disturbance rather than relying on the chemical crutch of sleeping tablets. Short-term, in times of crisis, medication can help. Long-term, the quality of sleep and life itself can be impaired.

1) Try to identify the 'cause' of your insomnia.
2) Remember your sleep pattern at a time in the past

when it was good (e.g., 7 hours a night). Devise a schedule whereby you get up *at the same time every day, including the weekend* regardless of how much you have slept. If it is just your biological clock that is disturbed, a rigorous schedule is often the solution.

3) Alcohol disrupts sleep. Reducing or avoiding alcohol can help enormously.

4) It is estimated that smokers take much longer to fall asleep, a difference of more than half an hour. Reducing or quitting can help.

5) Buy a good bed. It is interesting that the one piece of furniture that is often never replaced is the one we spend one-third of our lives using. A firm mattress and a good pillow really help our sleep.

6) Have a routine. The old remedies of a hot bath, a warm glass of milk are still good.

7) Heavy curtains to block out light in summer are advised. The circadian rhythm is light-related and associating sleeping with the 'dark' hours helps our pattern.

8) Seasonal Affective Disorder, or SAD, is a type of depression which is associated with the winter months and directly related to less sunlight. Several studies suggest that very bright artificial light can be effective in treatment. Special high intensity fluorescent light boxes which can be bought are used and reported to also help with sleep.

9) A similar-type treatment called 'The Downing Technique' is also regarded as an effective light treatment. Amongst other things, it has been associated with helping sleeping patterns.

10) If tension and a stressful lifestyle are part of your sleeping problem, then this needs to be addressed. There are many stress management and relaxation programmes available in Ireland. You could opt for biofeedback which involves the use of instruments to teach control over bodily stress reactions. Others find autogenic training (relaxing through imagination and auto-suggestion) or progressive muscular relaxation (breathing and tightening and relaxing muscle groups) or cognitive therapy

(changing your thinking and stress reactions) helpful. A change in stressed lifestyle often produces a change in sleeping style.

11) We know that caffeine in coffee, tea and in cola drinks can aggravate and cause sleep problems. Decaffeinated drinks, or drinking herbal drinks, may help.

12) If possible, don't go to bed hungry or after a heavy meal.

13) Exercise, even a walk, before the bedtime routine often helps.

14) Some people are very sensitive to ions in the atmosphere. Electronic ionizers can be bought which can help sleep.

15) Soothing aromas or aromatherapy can enhance sleep and there are many varieties available from health stores in Ireland.

16) For simple snoring, you might find it useful to attach a clothes-peg or a similar object to the back of your nightclothes. This will encourage you to roll onto your sides. This can be helpful since snoring is exacerbated by lying on your back.

17) For some people, trying to stay awake, rather than trying to go to sleep, works. Keeping the eyes open tires them and induces us to close them. It may be that this 'reverse psychology' will help. Which is worse, thinking you can't sleep or thinking you *must* stay awake?

18) Confront the issues in your life which may be 'causing' your sleep breakdown.

The range of psychological distress is as wide as life itself. Sleep can be disturbed when early childhood experiences, feelings of being unloved or unlovable, of being neglected, or rejected are re-evoked. Experiences of fear, of attack, of abandonment, of failure, of loneliness and isolation often first present themselves as sleep problems. Those of us who work as therapists have the privilege of talking to people at this time. Whatever your sleep problem, whatever its cause, suffering silent sleepless nights is not necessary. The task is to uncover the root of the problem. Undertaking therapy can lead to resolution, or as Sarah said in the radio programme accompanying this book, 'I feel there's a means to an end. I'll be fine'.

Further Reading

Cartwright, Rosalind Dymond, *A Primer on Sleep and Dreaming*, Addison–Wesley, Reading, Mass. and London, 1978.

Monk, Timothy H. (editor), *Sleep, Sleepiness and Performance*, John Wiley & Sons, Chichester, 1991.

Cohen, David B., *Sleep and Dreaming. Origins, Nature and Functions*, Pergamon Press, Oxford, 1979.

Foulkes, David, *The Psychology of Sleep*, Scribner, New York, 1966.

Crisp, A. H. and Stonehill, E., *Sleep, Nutrition and Mood*, Wiley, London, 1976.

Trauer, Dr Tom, *Coping with Stress. A Family Guide to Healthy Living*, Salamander Books, London and New York, 1986.

STRESS IN THE WORKPLACE

EDWARD HOGAN

PSYCHOLOGICAL HEALTH IS DETERMINED by many factors: circumstances of birth and upbringing, schooling, friendships and support, physical well-being, the fostering of talent and the nurturing of emotional expression. Allied to these is the attainment of a reasonable level and standard of living so as to enable the development of personal resources and talents. So when we come to look at work and stress, we may find that for those who are unemployed, particularly on a long-term basis and with limited or no access to those essentials for self and family, the subject at hand may be seen as trivial or as a luxury which society can ill afford.

Epidemiological studies, i.e., studies aimed at measuring the rates and prevalence of illness in society, consistently indicate the lower levels of psychological health among the long-term unemployed when compared with similar age groups and social groups among the employed population. Unemployment brings its own serious and extensive range of problems including depression, anxiety, irritability, lack of concentration and an increasing sense of hopelessness, which often improve quickly on re-entry to the world of work. However, the issue of unemployment, tragic as it is, is outside the scope of this chapter which focuses on stress in relation to those at work.

What is the size of the work stress problem? It is difficult to accurately answer this question especially in an Irish context where figures for absenteeism rarely include non-medical causes.

International estimates suggest a range of figures. Kearns (1986), in a UK context, suggests that up to 60% of absenteeism from work is caused by stress-related disorders and that in the UK alone up to 100,000,000 working days are lost because people cannot cope with what faces them at work.[1] Cooper (1986) suggests that up to £1.5bn is lost as a result of alcoholism in industry and that American employers spend approximately $750m replacing employees below the retirement age due to coronary heart disease.[2] If we consider the repeated links of stress to such conditions as hypertension and heart disease, stomach difficulties, increased use of tobacco and alcohol and various psychological conditions, notably anxiety and depression, then we begin to see the possible repercussions at work when stressful conditions are prevalent.

Costs to an organisation include absenteeism and labour turnover, increased health care costs, loss of energetic workers and a workforce becoming increasingly burned out. An organisation with deterioration in communication often experiences poor judgement and decision-making. We will later look at specific sources of stress at work and possible interventions to alleviate this distress when it occurs.

WHAT IS STRESS?: A very quick review of the area suggests a gradual evolution in the defining of stress over the last half century. Initially, it was deemed as a non-specific response of the body to any demand placed upon it. A later addition suggested that it was the state of the organism when reacting to new circumstances and, still later again, it was suggested as a particular relationship between the person and the environment that is appraised by the person as exceeding his or her resources and endangering his or her well-being. Before we move to what might be now considered a good working definition of stress, let us take a number of examples:

The person locked in a lift of a tall building with no

1 Kearns, J., *Stress at Work: The Challenge of Change*, BUPA Series, The Management of Health: 1, Stress and the City, BUPA, London, 1986.
2 Cooper, C. L., *Job Distress*, Bulletin of the British Psychological Society, 39, p. 325–31, 1986.

control over exit.

The student striving for A's in examinations.

The athletes straining to reach the tape.

The assembly-line operator attempting to maintain pace with the conveyor belt.

The former team player turned team manager.

The university-trained or college-trained researcher promoted to production or personnel management.

The non-consultant hospital doctor who works on temporary six month placements with no permanent contract.

David Fontana, in his excellent book *Managing Stress*, gives us a very good working definition of stress which relates to all of the above examples.[3] He states that stress is a demand made upon the adaptive capacities of the mind and/or body. If these capacities can handle and enjoy the stimulation involved then stress is helpful and welcome. However, if such capacities cannot cope and find the demands debilitating then stress is deemed to be unwelcome and unhelpful. This particular definition allows us to link a number of relationships. It suggests strongly that stress involves demands made either externally or internally and the individual's physical or psychological capacities to respond to, cope with and absorb the demands when they come. In each of the above examples we find that when the individual's capacities are adequate to the demands then the individual continues to function and surmount the obstacles as they are encountered. By contrast, when the individual finds that he or she does not possess such requisite capacity, then he or she falls victim to the situation and may be deemed to be distressed as a result.

The consequences of too much stress include:

A. At a Physical Level

Sleep disturbance – difficulty getting off to sleep, early

---

3 Fontana, David, *Managing Stress*, British Psychological Society and Routledge, London, 1988.

morning waking.

Appetite changes including a loss of appetite or over-eating when under pressure.

Digestive disturbance including stomach cramps, diarrhoea, constipation.

Chest pain which may indicate a serious underlying cause.

Headaches.

Reduction in energy levels.

Death: A recent addition to the stress at work literature comes from Japan; *Karoshi,* meaning death from overload, is claiming an increasing number of lives among relatively healthy middle-aged working men.

B. Emotional Indicators

Increase in tension.

Mood changes either of an angry, irritable and explosive nature or withdrawn, reclusive and depressed.

A sharp fall in self-esteem or self-worth.

A growing sense of helplessness over the direction of one's life.

A gradual bottling up of one's own feelings and a lack of confidence to express these in any company.

C. Indicators at Work

Deterioration in relationships with colleagues.

Changes in attitudes to clients, pupils or patients.

Reduction of performance and minimalist attitude to work.

Decrease in concentration and attention-span and consequent increase in errors made.

Poor organisation and planning.

Increasing hostility to work and its environment.

Reduction in attention to instructions or new information/technology.

Gradual disengagement from work leading to increased absenteeism.

An increasing sense of personal failure.

Disparagement of own or other's achievements.

MOST WRITERS IN THE field of stress and its management refer to the importance of personality in influencing the outcome of stress on behaviour. Various personality types have emerged as front runners or leaders in terms of proneness to stress. While research remains rather thin on whether or not personality is a significant factor, nevertheless there is a consistency in the reporting of a number of characteristics or types which feature in the stress literature.

The most widely known personality type in recent years is that described as 'Type A Personality', originating in the work of two cardiologists, *Friedman* and *Rosenman*, who first described this individual, usually male, often middle-aged, appearing more frequently in their cardiac clinics.[4] Before we look more closely at such characteristics perhaps you might like to answer a number of questions in a very simple 'yes' or 'no' fashion:

1) Are you often physically tense?
2) Do you find it difficult to listen and wait for others to finish their sentences? Do you often want to interrupt or hurry them to a conclusion?
3) Can you delegate at work or must everything be done by you?
4) Can you take time off and do you enjoy leisure activity? Are your holidays welcomed as relaxing interludes or are they seen as a necessary evil?
5) Is winning more important to you than participating?
6) Had you time for your lunch today or was it taken at your desk or at a meeting or in driving from A to B?

Type A personalities have been described as those who are characterised by an intense need to achieve at any cost: they are highly competitive and often seen as Machiavellian in their methods; aggressive and demanding, they are perceived as extremely hostile. With high standards demanded of themselves and others they may be quite competent in

---

4 Friedman, M. and Rosenman, R. H., *Type A Behaviour and Your Heart*, Alfred A. Knopf, New York, 1974.

areas of task analysis and completion but tend – because of their aggressiveness – to have poor social relationships and consequently are poor team members or team leaders.

Type A's have a huge sense of time urgency. Time, in fact, is a dominant theme in their lives with a marked obsession about time-wasting. Consequently, everything is done at pace: talking, driving, eating, conducting of meetings. They also feel that they are forced to do more and more in less and less time.

Type A's tend to be hasty, impatient and impulsive and because of their poorly developed sense of reflectiveness are poor at judging failure or error. Lacking in insight they often appear to be punitive personalities, i.e., blaming others for mistakes made as there is no room for acknowledgement of error on their own part. As stated earlier, cardiologists have recognised them as increasingly more frequent users of cardiac units, but apart from the impact on their physical health Type A behaviour also has other side-effects. Such behaviour tends to permeate other areas of the individual's life, often making Type A personalities poor parents, husbands/wives, lovers, friends. In general, Type A's tend to propagate stress reactions and may not be your favourite companion for a Saturday night out or two weeks in the sun. *Two weeks in the sun – Lord how could I afford to be away from work for ...*

A SECOND AND VERY interesting type which has been described is that of the 'Hardy Personality'.[5] Here is a further attempt to link disposition or temperament with behaviour and stress – it is characterised by the possession of a number of traits including:

Commitment as opposed to alienation.
Control as opposed to powerlessness.
Challenge as opposed to threat.

This approach suggests that, among persons facing signi-

---

5 Maddi, S. R. and Kobasa, S. C., *The Hardy Executive, Health Under Stress*, Dow Jones/Irwin, Homewood, Illinois, 1984.

ficant stressors, those high in hardiness will be significantly less likely to fall ill either mentally or physically than those who lack hardiness, i.e., those who display alienation, powerlessness or threat in the face of change. This theory further suggests that those possessing such a style of personality develop an extensive repertoire of coping as they always perceive change, real or threatened, as something to be met in a positive or constructive fashion and, hence, are rarely disabled or debilitated by it. If we refer to an earlier description or definition of stress we can see how this 'Hardy Personality' would welcome rather than avoid such change when it comes.

Another interesting attempt at linking personality with stress comes from Warr, who distinguishes between a number of aspects of an individual's mental health which help to protect the individual against distress or breakdown.[6] These include:

Affective well-being.
Competence.
A sense of autonomy or independence.
Level of aspiration.

Warr suggests that psychologically healthy people are aware of their emotional strengths and weaknesses as well as having the capacity to appropriately express emotion. Likewise, they learn the limits of their knowledge and expertise and feel competent in many of the areas in which they are engaged. In decision-making there is the possession of a sense of autonomy and independence and, finally, a continuing interest in improvement and the pursuit of new knowledge and expertise.

IS YOUR TYPE A Boss/Husband beyond Redemption? David Fontana, in *Managing Stress*, outlines a number of ways in which the Type A personality can attempt to manage his life

---

6 Warr, P. B., *Work, Unemployment and Mental Health*, Oxford University Press, Oxford, 1987.

a little better. He emphasises *humour* as a first prerequisite for change. Type A personalities tend to be very dour, serious individuals who fail to see humour in any situation. The ability to laugh at oneself is invaluable in this respect and needs to be fostered and encouraged. A second suggestion centres on the need to broaden one's horizons – as outlined above, Type A's tend to be narrowly focused. In looking at healthy families or organisations we find understanding and respect for others as a key ingredient in the make-up of successful units. The Type A individual, short on altruistic features, needs to be coached in the ways of perspective appreciation. Delegation of work tends to be foreign to the Type A personality. 'Nobody does it better than I', is the motto which needs to be revised.

Furthermore, the development of leisure time for its own sake, perhaps involving rushing to the gym at lunchtime, may not be what is required in this particular case. Time out, or time off, may be more valuable than the pursuit of compulsory leisure.

When we examine the areas of work likely to lead to distress in the individual's life we find that the possibilities are myriad. As jobs and organisations differ, so too do the potential causes of difficulty. What is especially problematic for members of one company or organisation can be no problem to others. Indeed, within similar jobs or professions, organisational climate can determine whether such stressors ever come to the surface. Identification of stressors at work can be facilitated if we look at a number of approaches:

1) Are the stressors at work
   (a) Of recent origin or
   (b) Ongoing and persistent over time.
2) Are the stressors linked to
   (a) Poor physical conditions, unrealistic time demands, sheer volume of work – work overload, lack of stimulation, too little to do.
   (b) Personal development within the job, including lack of recognition or reward for experience, knowledge or expertise.

Poor promotional outlets.

Lack of adequate career structure – a pyramid effect, with too many caught at the base.

Being promoted beyond one's level of competence with resultant personal distress and related effects on others.

Increased use of temporary status thereby increasing job insecurity.

(c) Relationships in the world of work.

Poor relationship skills.

Conflict with superiors.

Feelings of victimisation over which the individual is powerless.

Difficulties with peers/colleagues.

Inability to delegate to others effectively.

Sexual harassment issues, especially for female employees.

(d) Role problems.

Lack of clarity of role in team or organisation.

Role conflict.

(e) Other general areas likely to cause distress, including:

Inadequate preparation and training for change.

Powerlessness in decision-making.

Lack of variety and monotony in the workplace or job.

Poor leadership – either absent or hostile/vindictive.

Inability to cope with responsibilities of job, especially involving the lives or futures of others.

Perfectionism – subscribing to the myth that one is only valuable as a person if one is 100% accurate, right, or correct in everything undertaken.

(f) Interface of work and non-work factors, especially work/home link.

Research into the specifics of job stress linked with occupation indicate differences which can be referred to here. Shostak, for example, outlines four principal concerns for blue collar workers, namely:[7]

7 Shostak, A. B., *Blue Collar Stress*, Addison–Wesley, Reading, Mass., 1980.

1) A person's pay.
2) A person's safety at work.
3) The quality of the work-setting, including noise, light, temperature, toxicity.
4) Job stability.

White collar workers, particularly at managerial level, appear to share many of the previously outlined problem areas, but in recent times, other difficult issues have joined the list, including:

Problems in relation to mergers and acquisitions.
Retrenchment and budget cutbacks.
Job insecurity.
The inability to move from a closed or locked-in position
– i.e., no possibility of change.

In looking across both white collar and blue collar working areas, it is notable that many writers refer to an underlying, yet important source of stress among many workers and that is the growing uncertainty about the future of one's own job. Certainty in the workplace has diminished considerably in the past decade. Jobs, firms, industries and businesses, previously seen as safe and secure, have been threatened – many have succumbed to economic change and either declined or disappeared. Workers in the public service, in banking, in farming and in the traditional industries have all had to face new demands and more difficult decisions. In such an uncertain working world it is inevitable that many workers will feel increasing tension and distress. Some individuals, faced with such profound changes in their occupational and economic fortunes and reaching a stage in their lives where the chances of re-employment are slim, have slipped helplessly into a depressive-like state, sometimes resulting in self-harm or suicide. Recent Irish research indicates a growing alienation among unemployed people from the core or central values of the surrounding society where hopelessness is becoming more commonplace vis-a-vis expectations of work.

Our earlier definition of stress linked the relationship

between demand and the capacity of the individual to meet such demand, and in general when we look at stress at work we find that such a definition continues to be relevant. When we look closely at the literature in this area we find that there is a considerable link between demand and control in determining stress outcomes in the individual's life. By 'control' we mean the amount of latitude an individual has in decision-making within his job or organisation. The suggestion coming forward is that those individuals who are in high demand but low control jobs suffer the highest degrees of stress-related illnesses. Those in high demand but equally high control jobs seem to fare much better in that, while producing relatively high stress levels, they also seem to achieve higher levels of fulfilment both inside and outside of work. In contrast, those generally in low demand jobs or occupations tend to complain of boredom and loss of interest in work although reporting of stress symptoms is low and indeed, in many cases, relatively non-existent. This approach might remind us that when we look at work stress, it isn't something which is just confined to executives, managing directors or world leaders: in fact, it is more likely to remind us of the hazardous, dangerous and over-burdened occupations which do not enjoy the public limelight and may not be immediately perceived as inherently stressful in themselves.

What do we do when faced with a growing problem at work resulting from one or more of the sources outlined above – in general, there are two avenues open to us: we change or the environment changes. When faced with a problem or crisis we can choose from a number of options:

A. Inertia – do nothing, it might go away!
B. Denial – what problem? Who said I/we had a problem in the first place?
C. We can attempt to solve the problem – this cannot continue, I must do something about it.

In occupational stress, the person needs to look down a number of roads if successful resolution is to occur – what can I do to change, alter or resolve the problem or what can my team, company, firm, organisation do to change, alter or resolve the problem?

Interventions in the workplace are divided into three broad categories:

1. Employee Assistance Programmes.
2. Stress Management Training for Employees.
3. Reduction of number/level of stressors experienced by organisational members as a whole.

EMPLOYEE ASSISTANCE PROGRAMMES (EAP'S) have been a growing feature of American industrial life since the 1950s. It is estimated that approximately 9,000 US companies are actively involved in such programmes, while in Britain there has been a similar mushrooming in both the public and private sectors. Initially, such programmes centred almost exclusively on alcohol-related problems and the consequent costs to the company or organisation. In more recent times, what is described as 'a broad brush' approach has developed within such programmes endeavouring to address other personal problems as well as addictions.

A recent and impressive example of such a development in Britain is the Stress Care Programme operated by the Maudsley Hospital in London in conjunction with Care Assist, a telephone advice service which is a branch of the Royal Insurance Group of companies. This service provides employees with free, confidential, professional advice on most subjects in their private or working lives – a service which is paid for by the employer.

Employees are given coded numbers which protect their confidentiality, but calls can be analysed by problem, company and department, thereby giving employers a picture of patterns of distress within their own organisations.

Professional counsellors are recruited to man the service which is available 24 hours a day, 365 days a year.

European companies are beginning to look at the American experience which suggests a cost saving of some $6 for every dollar spent in EAP's.

What constitutes a good EAP? L.R. Murphy (1988), writing in Cooper and Payne's book, *Stress at Work,* suggests the following:[8]

Commitment and support from top management.
A clear, written set of policies and procedures that outlines the purpose of the EAP and how it functions in the organisation.
Close cooperation of unions.
Training of supervisors on their role in problem identification.
Education of employees, and the promotion of the EAP service to foster widespread utilisation throughout the company.
A level of care which includes referral to community agencies and follow-up services where necessary.
A clear policy on confidentiality of employee information.
The coverage of EAP services by company health insurance benefits.

In more recent times, there appears to be a growing interest and commitment to such programmes within the Irish work environment – a development which is both welcome and deserving of support. The expansion of such a service throughout different working sectors may facilitate the development of a healthier workforce and, in turn, a healthier working organisation.

In general, programmes aimed at improving stress management within the individual and the workforce have two major aims:

A. To foster awareness in the individual of where stress originates, its action and outcome.
B. To teach a range of skills in combating this stress.

Ideally, we could see this approach not simply as an inter-

8 Murphy, L. R., writing in Cooper, C. L. and Payne, R. (eds), *Stress at Work,* Wiley, Chichester, 1988.

vention after the event but also as a possible preventative measure. What we are encouraged to do is look at lifestyle and recognise potential sources of difficulty before they become actual and disabling. Eastern traditions of fostering mental and physical daily exercise have much to teach us in this respect.

The essential theme permeating stress management programmes is that of 'self-care'. In this respect we need to address the 'self' at a number of levels.

A. PHYSICAL WELL-BEING

Am I looking after my diet? Am I eating regularly and sensibly, avoiding the 'enemies' – fats, nicotine, excess caffeine and alcohol. Do I have a regular and adequate consumption of water to prevent dehydration.

Do I take time to exercise regularly and at a level appropriate for my age and current level of fitness (or lack of it)?

'Don't try to live the afternoon of your life according to the programme of the morning' (*Jung*).

What do I do for relaxation – walk, look at nature, read, engage in non-work pursuits: possible use of yoga, transcendental meditation (TM), relaxation training.

B. THE SOCIAL SELF

The place of friends in my life – do I look for social/personal support where I can release or 'let go' of emotional build-ups?

Do I have a pressure valve through my friendships?

Has work increasingly isolated me from social contact both within and outside the family? Am I like the father and son in Harry Chapin's song, 'The Cat's in the Cradle' – always waiting for the appropriate time to begin or continue relationships – we'll get together then, soon, tomorrow ...

Have things slipped beyond the level of self-help and is the service of an outside individual or agency required?

ROBIN SKYNNER, IN HIS work on family dynamics and

therapy, develops a theme or concept of the healthy family.[9] In his more recent work he endeavours to apply such a theme to organisations and argues that what is true for families can be applied to larger units such as offices, schools, banks, factories and corporations. What emerges is very applicable to successful teamwork at most levels. Principal themes emerging include:

   1. *Strong and clear leadership:*
   Authority is clearly vested in the parents but exerted through negotiation rather than rigid authoritarian structures.
   2. *Communication which is clear and relatively free of 'noise' or distortion:*
   Emphasis is placed on the *reception* as well as the *transmission* element of communication, i.e., feedback is given and invited in turn.
   3. *Clear and precise drawing of boundaries, leading to comfortable assumption of roles:*
   If I am the child I know I am the child – I am not asked to be the parent.
   4. *High degrees of mutual acceptance and understanding.*

Some commentators in the area of work and stress would suggest that the above interventions are merely papering over cracks or offering at best a temporary solution to what are really deeper and more resistant issues. Consequently, they argue for a more radical redress of the problems by suggesting interventions at the level of the organisation itself.

One might immediately agree, thinking it logical to remove the source of the problem, thereby dispensing with employee targeted interventions altogether. However, it is not quite that simple. Resistance to such fundamental change is often based on financial or economic determinants, e.g., reduction of atmospheric pollution emanating from local production facilities may mean increased costs, reduced profits,

---

9 Skynner, Robin, *Explorations with Families*, Tavistock/Routledge, London, 1988.

possible job losses or even closure. The ongoing debate in Britain (and in Ireland) about the THORP nuclear facility may be taken as an example, but one need not look only at production facilities in the chemical or nuclear industry. Some years ago, and after much negotiation, a branch of the public service was rehoused from a location deemed to be a 'sick building' where the level of illness was deemed to be abnormally high. Provision of increased adequate lighting and heating, adequate canteen and changing facilities, shorter hours, reasonable rest-breaks, provision of tachographs in cabs and trucks all could be taken as structural changes facilitating a reasonable quality of life to those in such employment.

FROM THE OUTSET OF this chapter the theme of control, or lack of it, has been linked to the development of stress. Considerable evidence has accumulated indicating that those in high demand and low control jobs yield much higher levels of distress than those who retain appropriate control within their task or their job. What do we mean by control? L. R. Murphy selects a number of criteria:

1) How the job is done.
2) How the work is scheduled.
3) Selection of methods used in performing tasks.
4) Timing of work/rest breaks.
5) Arrival and departure times.
6) Modification of unpleasant physical conditions.
7) Job mobility.
8) Independence in areas of decision-making.

The cynical observer, at this point, may feel that the above are the perfect recipe for idleness and laziness within the working environment. However, quite the contrary is observed, where such factors operate to increase cooperation, group participation and generally higher morale within the workforce. With the reported increase in stress litigation and the escalating costs of employee health care insurance, many companies across many countries are providing extensive health care, stress prevention and physical fitness program-mes for employees. Fewer companies actually engage in stress prevention or counselling programmes, but some employ outside services to help meet employees' needs. A slow, but gradual recognition of such needs is occurring in Ireland in public and private sector companies. Looking after the health of individual family members contributes ultimately to the health of that family itself, thus enabling it to achieve maximum potential. Therein lies a tale.

OCCUPATIONAL BURNOUT: THE TERM 'BURNOUT', as applied to work, has increasingly appeared in the psychological literature as well as in the deliberations of many frontline professions in recent times. It is becoming increasingly accepted that occupational burnout is a stress-related response and is not something new or independent of it. It has been described as an 'umbrella' term to cover emotional, cognitive, physical and behavioural changes in the person's life, always of a negative variety and frequently with debilitating consequences.

It was first described in the early 1970s especially in professions or jobs involving constant service to, and of, other people. How do we recognise this in ourselves or in our colleagues? Maslach and Edelwich, two of the early leaders in the field, describe a number of key ingredients:[10]

A. *Emotional Exhaustion:* the individual has a tired, worn out response to what is perceived as chronic emotional strain. Maslach indicates this increase in emotional overload as the key factor. Here, the individual tries to cope by retreating into superficial, easy or quick methods of problem-solving rather than working through problems as previously would have been the case.

B. *Depersonalisation:* this term is not to be confused with that found in anxiety or schizophrenia – it refers to the increased

10 Maslach, Christina, *Burnout: The Cost of Caring*, Prentice-Hall, New Jersey, 1982.
Edelwich, J., *Burnout: Stages of Disillusionment in the Helping Professions*, Human Sciences Press, New York, 1981.

detachment the worker feels to the individuals he or she deals with. The individual worker becomes colder and more distant and, if it becomes allied to a negative perception of others, then work becomes increasingly harder to do and is increasingly avoided.

C. *Reduced Personal Accomplishment:* a change is reported from high ideals and accomplishments to settling for much less. Self-esteem drops and self-criticism increases.

Burnout, according to Edelwich, is a progressive loss of idealism, energy and purpose experienced by people in various frontline jobs or professions. It should be noted that it is not an inevitable phenomenon, nor is it linear in progression. Some individuals can be more prone to this than others and, indeed, it may happen to the same individual on a number of different occasions. Burnout, as the term implies, is very gradual, it doesn't happen suddenly – it is a gradual, downhill process. Importantly, it is reversible. Fatalism in the use of the concept causes a negative set in the minds of those to whom it is applied. How else might we recognise it in ourselves?

A. In its mildest form it is experienced by many at work. Minute changes in physical and psychological health may be noted but may frequently be of very short duration and are often corrected after a holiday or a short-term break from the work environment itself.

B. When signs and symptoms last a little longer, it is harder to deal with. There is an increase in fatigue, headaches, over-anxiety about work, anger in relation to individuals at work – either clients or colleagues, reduction in job performance, an increase in cynicism and possible increased reliance on alcohol or other legally-prescribed medication. There can be a general feeling of being used by others and, in turn, getting very little for oneself. Should this persist over time then there is movement to a third level where the patterns are becoming increasingly entrenched and are less likely to change of their own accord. A sinister development at this point is the alienation from all that was personally valued. It may also mark the beginning of the spread of the difficulty to areas outside of work and the individual is fast approaching what Maslach calls 'terminal burnout'. If this is the case then self-help is not enough. Holidays, time-off or new hobbies will not adequately address the difficulty.

As with other areas of physical and psychological difficulties, early intervention is ideally the choice to be made. We need to monitor the changes in our behaviour, changes already outlined in our physical, social, emotional, cognitive and general working selves. Ignoring such changes as they occur generally serves to maintain the problem. Failure to initiate action will almost certainly guarantee a move from an early or initial stage right through to the later or terminal stages. Recognition of the problem by careful monitoring, and acceptance of information or feedback coming from within ourselves or from reliable sources within our environment at home or at work, is a first prerequisite. Thereafter, thorough or careful analysis of both the source and the course of the problem may allow us to initiate appropriate action. Such an approach usually precludes adoption of 'false interventions', including drug or alcohol usage, increased absenteeism or the belief that leaving one's job is the solution. In adopting a problem-solving approach, the individual is in reality choosing to accept responsibility for his or her own needs and their fulfilment. In a work setting this does not mean that one is responsible for the current working conditions but is responsible for accepting reality as it is and doing something about it now. This may lead to changes in the relationship one has with the work environment which in turn may help to reinstate a renewed relationship with work.

THIS CHAPTER HAS BEEN about stress and the workplace. Throughout, the dominant theme has been that of the relationship between demand and the individual's capacity to meet that demand. Demand is not confined only to executive or managerial roles but is inherent in most, if not all, work situations. The changing world of work in the latter part of the twentieth century, full of uncertainty and change, will increasingly tax the capacities of most. The challenge for all of us lies in devising and implementing adequate programmes aimed at maintaining and increasing the health of the individual and the organisation. Let us hope we perceive it as challenge and not threat, stimulating rather than debilitating, thus ensuring better work structures and environments in the future.

Further Reading

Cooper, C. L., Cooper, R.D. and Eaker, L.M., *Living with Stress*, Penguin Books, London, 1988.

Cooper, C. L. and Payne, R., *Stress at Work*, Wiley, Chichester, 1988.

Fontana, David, *Managing Stress*, British Psychological Society and Routledge, London, 1988.

Skynner, Robin, *Explorations with Families*, Tavistock/Routledge, London, 1988.

OBSESSIVE COMPULSIVE DISORDER

FRANK O'DONOGHUE

MADNESS, AT LEAST IN its behavioural expression, is easily recognised by the layman. Most of us have had the experience of witnessing some unfortunate psychotic individual shambling along the street mumbling or shouting in response to hallucinatory voices which he hears. His behaviour, possibly his appearance and dress, indicate to us that he is clearly mentally unwell. Even the layman will appreciate that this form of mental problem is quite different from what might loosely be called the anxiety disorders. Here, while the person may be greatly distressed, contact with reality is retained, the rules of logic apply and the person has considerable insight. The difference between the two groups is their willingness to seek treatment; in the case of the former, patients may need considerable coaxing before they can be engaged in treatment, while in the latter the discomfort to the patient is far more likely to cause him to seek out treatment.

There is, however, one type of anxiety disorder where the behavioural idiosyncrasies of the patient are so bizarre that the layman could be forgiven for confusing it with some of the more severe, psychotic illnesses. This condition, obsessive compulsive disorder, will be the subject of this chapter.

Because of the wide range of human experience, it has been known for many years that people from different cultural backgrounds will express their psychological distress in different ways. Bringing it down to a smaller scale, even people from similar cultural backgrounds will display different symptomatology – in other words, no two patients will display the same symptomatology. Unlike, say, appendicitis, where the individual has certain characteristic symptoms which lead one to the diagnosis, obsessive compulsive disorder (or indeed any emotional disorder) can present itself in a wide variety of ways.

OBSESSIVE COMPULSIVE DISORDER CAN be defined in the following terms: obsessions are (i) recurrent and persistent ideas, thoughts, impulses or images that are experienced, at least initially, as intrusive and senseless, for example, a parent having repeated impulses to kill a loved child, a religious person having recurring blasphemous thoughts; (ii) the person attempts to ignore or suppress such thoughts or impulses or to neutralise them with some other thought or action; (iii) the person recognises that the obsessions are the product of his or her own mind, not imposed from outside.

Compulsions have been defined as (i) repetitive, purposeful and intentional behaviours that are performed in response to an obsession, or in accordance to certain rules or in a stereotyped fashion; (ii) the behaviour is designed to neutralise or to prevent discomfort or some dreaded event or situation; however, either the activity is not connected in a realistic way with what it is designed to neutralise or prevent, or it is clearly excessive; (iii) the person recognises that his or her behaviour is excessive or unreasonable and, finally, the obsessions or compulsions cause marked distress, are time-consuming (take more than an hour a day) or significantly interfere with the person's normal routine, occupational functioning or usual activities or relationships with others.

We can see, therefore, that obsessive compulsive disorder (as the name implies) can be divided into a frequent intrusion of unwelcome, disturbing thoughts which, despite their best efforts, patients cannot dislodge and also compulsive behaviours, defined as actions (or sometimes avoidance) which patients feel relentlessly driven to carry out. Attempts to dispel the thoughts or disregard the compulsion are accompanied by intense feelings of anxiety.

How many people are affected by this condition? Because of natural feelings of embarrassment, people are reticent to acknowledge to others the extent of their emotional distress. For years, the prevalence of obsessive compulsive disorder was thought to be around 0.5% of the population. However, more recent studies have shown that many patients with the disorder do not seek treatment. One study suggested that those seeking treatment may be as low as 25% of sufferers (in comparison with 50% of depressives who will seek treatment). With this new information, the incidence is thought to be much higher (in the region of 2.5% of the population). There does not seem to be any marked bias towards one or other sex and the average age of onset of the condition is 20.

WHAT DO THEY COMPLAIN of, this 2.5% of the population? Earlier, the distinction between obsessional thoughts, on the one hand, and compulsive behaviours, on the other, was noted. In practice, the distinction between the two is seldom as clear-cut as that. Usually, the patient with an intrusive thought can only gain relief by either 'cancelling' the thought with another thought or by carrying out some stereotyped ritual. All of us have experienced at one time the niggling doubt that comes to mind when we are halfway to the airport on our holidays – did I leave the TV plugged in? did I check the back door to make sure it is locked? and so on. Most of us are happy to disregard the thought, unless we feel it is a very real possibility. Unfortunately, those who suffer from OCD will know no peace until they have returned and checked that everything is in order. At this point, the ordinary individual will happily go on his way, knowing he has done what is necessary. For the OCD patient, this is probably just the beginning of a series of ritualistic checks, usually completed a set number of times and in a highly ritualistic way.

A good example of this was the patient who was terrified that harm would come to his parents. Not alone did the thought of their death terrify him, but he was even more terrified at the idea that through some negligent action of his, they would die. Negligence for him meant the failure to carry out a series of complicated rituals. For example, if he were walking through a doorway, and the thought of his parents' death came to mind, he would feel compelled to stop, retrace his footsteps and go through the doorway again.

Unfortunately, this had to be carried out a set number of times, so one would frequently see him stopping, reversing through the door, going forward again, reversing again over and over until he felt that he had completed the ritual exactly in accordance with his strict rules and was then free to move on – free, that is, until the next obsessional thought triggered off a similar set of behaviours.

Obviously, such behaviour is time-consuming and, taken to the extremes listed above, can effectively cripple the patient. We have had patients who have washed their hands up to 150 times per day in a relentless pursuit of absolute hygiene, patients who had up to 500 items to check each night before they were satisfied that the house was locked, patients who hoarded large amounts of garbage and patients who were so terrified of harming others that every car journey was an excruciating experience, where they would drive forward 5 miles, then come back 3 miles, drive forward another 5 miles, back 3 and so on to prevent the off chance that they may have inadvertently and unknowingly brushed against a pedestrian or a cyclist and caused them injury.

WHY DO PEOPLE DEVELOP this disorder? Given the bizarre and often highly visible expression of the condition, and the fact that it is a neurosis and not a psychosis, it is not surprising that patients with obsessive compulsive neurosis were one of the first to attract the attention of Sigmund Freud, the father of modern psychiatry. If we look at a simplified version of Freud's map of the mind (see Figure 1 on next page) we can see how obsessive compulsive disorder fits into his schema of the neuroses. The large area to the right of the dotted line represents the unconscious mind, needing specialised psychoanalytic techniques to probe its extent. Located in the unconscious are the two basic instincts, the sexual instinct and the aggressive instinct which go together to make up the Id, which is constantly seeking expression. Located partly in the conscious mind but mainly in the unconscious mind lies the Super-ego, the Freudian equivalent

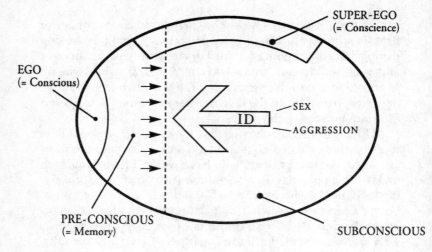

Figure 1

of our conscience. Under normal circumstances, the Super-ego acts as a check or brake on the demands of the Id. From time to time, however, the Id drives threaten to break out into our conscious awareness. This mobilises the neurotic defence of reaction formation. To put this in more simple terms, if one entertains hostile and aggressive impulses towards a parent, the conscious reaction to that might be an obsessive preoccupation with the safety of that very parent. Any further stirrings of the aggressive drive are met with an even more obsessional, meticulous approach to ensure the ongoing safety of the parent.

Using this model, treatment consisted of using psycho-therapy to probe the unconscious conflicts. Techniques such as dream interpretation, word association, free association and hypnosis were all used to tease out underlying conflicts. Freud wrote extensively about OCD – some of these papers, such as 'Totem and Taboo', which deals with the universal nature of obsessionality and in particular its relevance to religion, and also 'The Rat Man', provide anecdotal evidence of how Freudian therapy can help us understand obsessive compulsive disorder. Unfortunately, Freudian theory relied heavily on anecdotal evidence – hardly the type of material which would stand up to rigorous scientific scrutiny today. Nonetheless, it provided a working model which greatly helped our understanding of the condition and represented a giant leap forward.

THE NEXT MAJOR MILESTONE in the understanding of obsessive compulsive disorder was the contribution of the Learning Theorists. The Learning Theorists (or Behaviourists, as they became known) were not particularly interested in the unconscious but were (or tried to be) more concerned with observable, measurable data and, in particular, attempted to understand neurotic symptoms in terms of 'bad learning'. Indeed, much of their work springs from the animal experiments carried out by the Russian physiologist, Pavlov, who extensively studied conditioning in dogs. Initially, he would condition dogs to respond with physiological responses such as salivation to a previously neutral stimulus such as a bell. Later, he was able to condition neurotic symptoms in dogs and his work was replicated by others who subsequently began to apply these techniques in an attempt to understand how humans develop neurotic symptoms. In particular, considerable attention was paid to the role of anxiety. The Law of Effect showed that if an animal's behaviour is rewarded, the behaviour is likely to be repeated. B. F. Skinner took this a stage further by using the Skinner Box, where he found that he could shape the behaviour of animals by selectively rewarding them. Transferred to the human situation, psychologists began to talk of positive and negative reinforcement. Positive reinforcement was equated with a satisfactory state of affairs and, if this occurred after a behaviour, the behaviour was likely to be repeated. Investigators began to see that relief from anxiety was a very powerful reinforcer. As a result, researchers began to realise that if a behaviour (such as door checking or hand washing) is followed by a satisfactory state of affairs (reduction of anxiety) there is a strong possibility that the behaviour will be repeated. In some way, not yet understood, patients with obsessive compulsive disorder become addicted to this reduction in anxiety, so the behaviour is performed over and over again in a vain attempt to keep anxiety levels down.

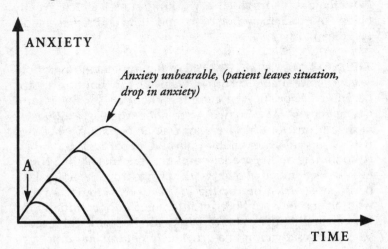

Figure 2

Figure 2 illustrates this diagrammatically. The vertical axis represents increasing anxiety, the horizontal axis represents time. At point A the patient experiences an anxiety provoking thought; this is followed by a steep increase in anxiety and the wish to carry out a compulsive behaviour (or think a 'cancelling thought'). Initially, the patient struggles against the urge to carry out the behaviour; this results in a steepening of the slope of anxiety until they can no longer tolerate the anxiety and carry out the compulsive behaviour. This may be washing or checking or whatever and results in a subsequent (temporary) drop in anxiety until the next intrusive thought triggers the cycle once more. With each repetition, the urge to carry out a compulsive behaviour is given in to earlier and earlier.

ON THE BASIS THAT the obsessional symptoms have been acquired by learning, it was felt reasonable to approach the treatment of these disorders from a learning viewpoint also.

Accordingly, therapists attempted to show patients that it was not necessary to complete the compulsive behaviour in order to achieve relaxation – if the urge to carry out the compulsive behaviour was resisted for a long enough period of time, the urge to carry it out would progressively diminish and eventually disappear. The solid lines in Figure 2 show what happens in OCD patients – the anxiety increases, the impulse is given into, there is a reduction in anxiety. On subsequent occasions, the compulsive behaviour is initiated at an earlier level in an attempt to avoid anxiety. Eventually, the patient is engaging in OCD behaviour most of the time.

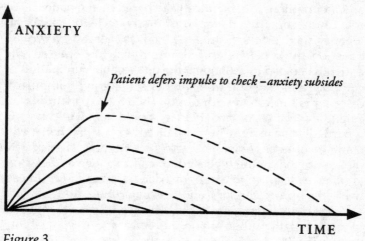

Figure 3

The dotted line in figure 3 shows what one can expect with therapy – if the impulse to check is deferred, the urge to check would progressively diminish. Subsequent exposure to the same learning experience will mean that zero anxiety will be reached sooner and sooner every time the patient successfully defers the urge to check/clean.

Other kinds of behaviour therapy were also used to shift these behaviours. On the basis that much of our learning is acquired by seeing behaviours modelled by significant figures (usually parents) as we grow up, therapists found that if

they demonstrated the correct behaviour to the patient, resolution of OCD occurred more quickly. This technique
(modelling), in addition to the technique described above
(cue exposure and response prevention), were the main approaches used in behavioural treatment for many years.

More recently, behaviour therapy has been usefully aug-
mented by the addition of the technique of cognitive therapy. Cognitive therapy seeks to identify faulty patterns of
thinking in which the patient engages and which perpetuate
the OCD syndrome. As with depression and anxiety disorders, patients with OCD are helped to identify negative
automatic thoughts. Prior to treatment, negative thoughts
and assumptions are uncritically accepted by the patient. The
role of the cognitive therapist is, firstly, to help the patient
identify such 'errors of thinking' and, as therapy evolves, to
question these beliefs and assumptions. In doing so, the
patient is helped to relinquish the obsessional rumination or
compulsive behaviour. In many cases, obsessive compulsive
disorder is concerned with responsibility; the patient is consumed by feelings of anxiety that, should he fail to carry out
a particular behaviour in a ritualised way, some harm will
come to others. Hence, many rituals involve checking to
make sure that nothing gets out of control, such as electrical
appliances leading to a fire, or bacteria passing on illness,
hence the bizarre checking and washing rituals, and so forth.

One of the approaches of a cognitive therapist would be
to ask the patient to examine this concept of responsibility
more critically, rather than automatically presume that he *is*
responsible. The obsessive compulsive patient is seen as having an exaggerated belief about the degree of harm that can
follow from certain thoughts which they might have. They
might believe that 'if I think about a certain event, failing to
prevent, or failing to try to prevent this happening is the
same as actually having done it'. These negative automatic
thoughts are plausible, almost believable and generate considerable anxiety in the patient. Only by taking precautions
(which are invariably excessive where OCD patients are
concerned) can they absolve themselves from the responsibility which they feel.

FOR MANY YEARS, OBSESSIVE compulsive disorder was regarded as simply a learned behaviour, i.e., a symptom which we were not born with but which, through early life experiences or the bad luck of faulty learning, left the patient with this crippling condition. However, even behaviour therapists would readily admit that when they apply these techniques to the treatment of phobias they can expect good results, but when the same techniques are applied to OCD sufferers the results do not match those achieved in phobic anxiety disorders. This, combined with the fact that there has been a known genetic element in OCD, has led people to seek an organic or physical basis for the condition. In recent years, the arrival of more sophisticated scanners, such as the nuclear magnetic resonance scans and the positron emission tomography scanners, have allowed investigators to look not just at the structure of the brain but also its chemical activity. In doing so, clear differences emerge between patients suffering from OCD and normal controls. In particular, the role of the neuro-transmitter serotonin has proved to be of crucial importance. A neuro-transmitter is a chemical messenger which is released from one nerve ending and jumps the gap to the next nerve ending, allowing the nerve impulse to complete its journey from one brain cell to another. There is a variety of neuro-transmitters in the brain of which serotonin is but one. Over the last 25 years, other neuro-transmitters have been investigated with particular respect to their role in depressive disorders. However, it is only relatively recently that serotonin and its role in OCD has come under scrutiny.

Apart from the use of scans, the technique of using 'chemical probes' has gained in popularity. Essentially, this consists of administering chemicals which will either enhance or interfere with the production of serotonin and monitoring the effects on obsessive compulsive symptoms. For some years, the anti-depressant drug, Clomipramine (Anafranil), was known to have an effect on obsessional symptoms, apart from any anti-depressant effect it might have. When serotonin crosses the gap from one cell to another, much of it is then lost through being absorbed into the brain cells. Clomipramine acts by preventing that loss, so that the serotonin is free to circulate over and over again. Unfortunately, Clomipramine affects several systems within the brain giving rise to a variety of sometimes unacceptable side-effects. In recent years, a new group of compounds, the selective serotonin re-uptake inhibitors has been developed. The SSRI's, as the name implies, selectively interfere with serotonin and this selectivity markedly reduces the incidence of side-effects. At present, large scale studies are being conducted to attempt to quantify the effect of these medications in OCD. The SSRI's currently available in Ireland include Fluoxetine, Fluvoxamine, Paroxetine and Sertraline.

NO REVIEW OF OBSESSIVE compulsive disorder would be complete without some reference to psychosurgery. For many years, it has been known that damage to certain nerve fibres can produce a change in behaviour. The first recorded case of this was the well-documented report on Phineas P Gage. Mr Gage was foreman on the Union Pacific Railway in the 1880s and his job was, firstly, to drill holes in rocks, then pack dynamite down into the hole with a steel rod before triggering the explosive charge. Unfortunately, on one occasion while stamping the dynamite down, the charge exploded and the steel bar was driven upwards through his forehead and out the top of his head! The remarkable fact was that he survived the episode at all and a medical report was published commenting on this fact. In the course of describing his residual symptoms, it was noted that from being a conscientious, somewhat perfectionist and over-controlled individual prior to the accident, he became 'coarse, foul-mouthed, given to liquor and intemperate habits'. The significance of this was not appreciated until some 50 years later when the effects of severing the connecting fibres to the frontal lobe were shown to reduce obsessional, perfectionist and over-controlled behaviour.

It may come as a surprise to many that psychosurgery is still used; in the 1940s and 1950s the technique was grossly overused and acquired a bad reputation as a result. By the early 1960s, the technique had fallen into almost complete disuse. However, since then, much more precise surgical interventions are possible and also the use of radioactive seeds to very selectively destroy certain fibres, reawakened an interest in this treatment. Nowadays, the technique is only used for severe, incurable cases of obsessive compulsive disorder who have had all other treatment modalities – behaviour therapy, psychotherapy, chemotherapy – and who remain in hospital crippled by their neurosis. In such cases, approximately two-thirds of patients will recover completely or almost completely with negligible, if any, adverse effects. However, behaviour therapy has to be continued during the post-operative care, sometimes for years to come if the patients are to maintain their gains.

AS CAN BE SEEN from the above, obsessive compulsive disorder has been investigated now for almost 100 years. This investigation has produced a wealth of information. By carefully sifting through this information, we can, with some confidence, make the following points:

1) Obsessive compulsive disorder affects approximately one in 40 people, males and females equally, and is as crippling in its severe manifestations as some psychotic conditions such as schizophrenia.
2) No clear-cut cause for the condition can be identified – genetic, interpersonal, learning and neuropharmacological theories have contributed to our understanding, leading us to believe that the condition is multifactorial in origin.
3) Treatment can be successful – cognitive behaviour therapy is the most likely to yield results, with the advent of the selective serotonin re-uptake inhibitor drugs promising further hope for OCD sufferers.
4) At the end of the day, it will probably be a combination of cognitive behavioural techniques plus chemotherapy which will give the greatest relief.

Further Reading
Foa, Edna B., PhD. and Wilson, Reid, PhD., *Stop Obsessing*, Bantam, New York, 1991.

Marks, Isaac, *Living with Fear*, McGraw Hill, Maidenhead, Berks., 1978.

ANOREXIA AND BULIMIA
A Developmental Approach

GILLIAN MOORE-GROARKE

FOR MOST PEOPLE IN the western world, eating is a natural, essential and enjoyable part of everyday life. Sadly, for an increasing number of women (especially teenage girls) and also a certain percentage of men (approximately one in ten with an eating disorder) food has become something to be feared and whenever possible avoided. This phobic avoidance response to food can eventually lead to complete physical and mental breakdown. For anorexic or bulimic patients, the obsession with weight, calories and food is so great that the obsession exists to the virtual exclusion of everything else in their lives. Whether sufferers are overweight, underweight or average weight, they all share the same fears of food and weight gain. They all desire extreme thinness, and they are all unhappy with themselves and their quality of life in general.

In the United States, six million people are recorded as having eating disorders, and in Britain there are one hundred and forty thousand registered anorexic and bulimic cases. In Ireland we have no absolute figures, but some studies estimate that among women between the ages of 15–30, one in five will develop an eating disorder at some stage of their lives. It is important also to remember that registers refer only to reported cases. Many sufferers live in secrecy for several years and because of the secretive element of eating disorder behaviour they may never report their illness. In truth, eating disorders are another form of breakdown.

ANOREXIA NERVOSA IS UNDEREATING to the point of starvation. It is characterised by a preoccupation with body weight and food, weight loss, intense fear of gaining weight, distorted body image and the cessation of monthly periods. It is most common among women who are between 12 and

25 years of age. Prevalence studies in the United States have indicated that for all males between the ages of 13 and 30, 1 in 390 has an eating disorder. There is a higher than normal incidence of eating disorders in males in certain subgroups which tend to emphasise slenderness or body image including: models, dancers, wrestlers, athletes, etc.

People suffering from anorexia attribute an abnormal significance to weight. They strive by dieting restraint to achieve an unreasonably low weight. Food intake develops into a distressing preoccupation and eating is associated with feelings of tension and guilt. Anorexics may weigh themselves frequently and constantly gaze at their shape in the mirror. Most are preoccupied with the subject of food and nutrition. They sometimes cook for the family, although they will not eat the food themselves. When they do eat, typically the food is cut into tiny pieces and consumed very slowly. Anorexics rarely lose their appetite, rather they overpower, indulging in excessive physical activity, specifically to lose weight. Sometimes the eating restraint is relaxed, then the anorexic submits to compulsive urges to overeat (binges). Following this, renewed vigorous dieting, exercise and self-induced vomiting occur in order to prevent weight gain. Some also get into laxatives/diuretics abuse in an attempt to lose weight.

On confrontation, the denial is enormous. Anorexics will deny any suggestion of a problem, and usually become highly manipulative in order to protect their anorexia. Deceitfulness shows its ugly head in order to protect weight loss, e.g., extra clothes or weights in the pockets. The onset of symptoms is likely to occur at times of stress. They socially isolate themselves, withdraw from reality and become perfectionists. These people are unhappy, lonely, confused, starving and need help! Emotionally, they are no older than the age at which the condition began – you might have a thirty year old presenting with anorexia which she has had for 15 years. Emotionally, they still think and behave like a 15 year old, because the obsession with food has totally encompassed their lives. Consequently, this immaturity can lead to relationship difficulties.

BULIMIA NERVOSA can best be defined as recurrent episodes of compulsive binge eating with or without self-induced vomiting and/or laxative abuse. People with bulimia can be of normal weight, overweight or underweight. They present themselves as superficially cheerful, composed and relaxed. Unlike the anorexics they usually seek help willingly and are usually relieved to be able to discuss their abnormal eating habits. They describe consuming vast amounts of high calorie foods. They overeat in private and may only finish when abdominal pain occurs. Self-induced vomiting can provide instant relief. Unfortunately, overeating and vomiting become habitual, occurring many times a day. Vast amounts of money can be spent and bulimics can be found to have financial difficulties. In a small number of cases, shoplifting, usually of food, has also been known to occur. In any one binge a bulimic can spend as much as thirty or forty pounds.

IT IS SUGGESTED THAT puberty marks the beginning of body dissatisfaction. Puberty, in itself, can be a difficult time for us all, but when accompanied by an eating disorder the whole developmental process breaks down. A developmental model emphasises the many stressors with which adolescents have to learn to cope. Pubertal weight gain, relationship changes, achievement threats and unrealistic ideals all coincide with age of onset of eating disorders. Other high risk periods include transition to secondary school or college, pregnancy, childbirth and separation from parents. Also, with the change in the cultural stereotype of the ideal female body, even young girls of normal weight are reporting dissatisfaction with their bodies. Peer influence is also an important factor. What I hope to look at is the different stages of adolescent development and examine how they relate to the development of eating disorders, when breakdown of these stages occurs.

In early adolescence (10–14 years), puberty initiates sexual maturity. The developmental process requires the adolescent to undergo and accept both physical and emotional changes. This is where the majority of cases of anorexia begin. An obvious question is, why do these adolescents want to starve themselves? Are they rejecting puberty as an attempt to prolong childhood? Are they avoiding sexual development, or struggling with their femininity or masculinity? In searching for answers to these questions, the causes of eating disorders have to be examined within the context of the individual, the family and society.

At puberty, the body triggers hormonal changes. Separation, identity and autonomy tasks increase conflict with adults. This also means managing these tasks along with sustaining a relationship with their parents. They must balance caring and taking responsibility for others with separation and autonomy, which is part of growing up and becoming an adult. This creates an added conflict for sufferers of eating disorders. At this age, they cannot create the balance that is required. Often they take responsibility for everybody else and neglect their own needs. In short, they are perfectionists and pleasers. Inside, rages an angry, confused, lonely person. For 90% of eating disordered women, there is a history of sexual abuse. The abuse creates boundary and relationship difficulties, both at a physical and emotional level. Pubertal changes are frightening. To the anorexic, delayed physical development is a relief, whereas bulimics might be promiscuous in their attempts to control feelings of rejection and isolation. In my own research I have found 50% of male bulimics with a history of sexual abuse.

These adolescents use food as a method of coping with bodily changes that trigger fear, feelings of being out of control, rejection and isolation. Attempts at control are made through self-destructive behaviours, which I have already mentioned in my definitions of these illnesses. Their families are both frantic and hopeless, and in many cases become even more overprotective.

Within the family, slimness is often reinforced. The children are taught to recognise that slimness is associated with success and power. Obesity is seen as a sign of weakness and overindulgence. In the context of society, beliefs such as 'If only I were thin, I would be happy' are to be challenged. A psycho-educational approach is required to teach against negative effects of stereotyping. This can be achieved at school level by inviting professionals to speak about eating disorders, or by meeting with parent groups.

Teenagers are often very idealistic and self-conscious. They think abstractly and in terms of multiple causality. Eating disorder patients, because of starvation, cannot achieve this successfully. They experience a decreased ability to concentrate, to think rationally and also suffer from very severe mood swings. It is often the mood swings which bring the eating disorder to the attention of parents. Because, for the most part, they are high achievers, if they cannot achieve 'perfect results' academically, they transfer their energy into achieving maximum control in terms of weight loss and dieting. I can remember a law student saying to me once that she felt the reasons her grades were improving every year was because she was losing more and more weight. This is an example of how irrational their thinking processes can become. Initially, I feel the emphasis should be on teaching the effects of eating disorders and on teaching awareness of healthy thinking, feelings and behaviours. Often patients are ignorant as to the medical complications and seriousness of their illness. Liaising with the patient's family doctor is also very important.

Often families practice negative communication patterns. Mothers are dissatisfied with their roles, fathers are absent or under-involved. In many cases this can lead to mothers and daughters becoming enmeshed, rather than interdependent. This in turn leads to low self-esteem and an inability to take the risk of expressing one's emotions. For years the anorexic or bulimic is told 'do not get angry', 'you shouldn't feel sad'. Expressing true emotions is perceived as attention-seeking behaviour. The adolescent represses his/her emotions and consequently learns not to take the risk of opening up in the future. This leads to enormous confusion regarding feelings and how to express them. Because of abuse in many cases, sexuality is feared rather than enjoyed. Perfectionism and high achievement replace natural sexual drives and because perfectionism is always nebulous, disappointment is usually the resulting emotion. Rather than perfection, I always stress to my patients to try to be the best 'they themselves' can be. Parents do a lot of good by reinforcing this belief among their children. The use of affirmations is a positive tool in enhancing good self-esteem.

Treatment should encompass a cognitive behavioural approach to teach conflict management and to express emotions assertively. It must also be pointed out that purging is a negative solution to managing stress. Choosing another solution is important. Purging can be replaced with many other behaviours, e.g., writing down how one feels, making a telephone call, going for a walk, etc ...

The therapist has to try and teach the adolescent that she is weak, obsessive and has not yet mastered dependency needs. Once the patient is ready for autonomy, the therapeutic relationship no longer has to foster dependence and nurturing traits. Mastery over emotions signifies progress. Reverting to obsessive behaviours again is a signal for nurturing but also for an authoritative stance from the therapist. The therapist or the parents cannot afford to be uncomfortable with confrontation. During family therapy, the therapist will teach the parents to master many of these skills.

THE 'SELF' IS DEFINED within a relationship with another person. Self-identity is based on values that come from the outside, rather than the inside. Values such as slimness, beauty, appearance and achievements are related to the body. Sex role identification becomes passive and dependent instead of assertive and interdependent. The pursuit of thinness through rigid adherence to diet and weight reflects someone who is suffering from low self-esteem, conflict over autonomy, control and separation issues. Rather than developing a sense of 'who I am' these teenagers ask, 'who should I be?' A good exercise here is to ask them to list some positive and negative things about themselves.

Therapy needs to acknowledge the need for caring about others, without discounting the self. The therapist also needs to push for identifying feelings and thoughts, and deciding on alternative behaviours. Within the family context it is important to create an open atmosphere where patients who are feeling vulnerable can go and discuss their feelings and receive support to engage in positive rather than negative behaviour patterns.

For anorexics, intimacy is feared and avoided because no internal self exists. Intimacy represents an invasion or intrusion into their personality. Therapy for eating disorders must begin by building trust, by building self-esteem, through the relationship. I have found in my own practice that this often takes at least one year. It may even take longer in the family context to regain trust that may have been broken.

For bulimics, intimacy is feared and avoided because the internal self is not trusted. Bulimics also fear that they will destroy others with their feelings. Relationships are far too intense and chaotic. They lose many friends because of their need to be in control all of the time, thus further enhancing feelings of isolation. With therapists they are often manipulative and the task in therapy becomes one of figuring out the result of such behaviour patterns. It is also important to contract with the patient basic ground-rules from the beginning. Supportive parents or partners can also make positive contracts, thus reinforcing the therapeutic goals within the family milieu.

Developing an ability to make a commitment appears in later adolescence, usually in the early twenties. On the outside, the anorexic or bulimic may seem mature, self-reliant, confident and strong. On the inside, the individual is in fact weak, conflicted and helpless. In therapy, if one learns to identify with the 'inner child', the adult can indeed be helped. Identification with the 'inner child' reduces the drive for perfectionism. Louise Hay, an American metaphysical therapist, promoted the use of this technique in learning to cope with cancer. In short, a commitment towards a reparenting model is required. This allows for resolution of early developmental tasks, i.e., trust, initiative and self-efficacy.

The developmental task is to shift from family to peer group and other adult figures. Eating disordered families resemble other families with psychiatric problems. There is generally a family history of alcoholism, sexual abuse, depression and suicide. Many eating disordered teenagers do not shift to their peer group because they are needed to stay close to home. Often in therapy they are extremely slow to act on the suggestion of moving out of home. Although many mothers genuinely want their sons and daughters to grow up and leave home, we find behaviours that suggest that if they did, their mothers would be left defenseless and isolated in their marriages. Parents outwardly say 'grow up', but at the same time treat them as young children. High protection and low caring foster high degrees of loyalty rather than support and nurturing. Food becomes both a friend and an enemy. Obsession with food keeps the focus on diet and on the self, rather than on peers. Therapy needs to reinforce independence and reassure family members that they can handle it. This is why I place such a huge emphasis on family therapy as well as individual consultations. When a meaningful relationship develops in therapy, parents generally relinquish their hold on their son or daughter. Generally, the fathers are reluctant to join in, but if left out, they will sabotage the gains made by both mother and child. Parents soon begin to realise their own difficulties and can deal with them. Usually, this occurs when the child has improved significantly. Often, at this stage, I would invite family members to attend for individual sessions to work on their own issues.

BEAUTY, SLIMNESS, WEIGHT CONSCIOUSNESS and denial of powerful internal needs, characterise anorexia nervosa and bulimia. The therapy should consider the relationship as the most powerful motivator and vehicle in which to support, nurture and encourage change. Cognitive restructuring techniques have also been found to be useful. They challenge irrational beliefs, such as 'slimness means power and success', 'if I eat regularly I will gain huge amounts of weight', and 'if I gain weight I will look more like an adult'. Parents will continuously be presented with these irrational beliefs, and must be consistent in their approach to dealing with them. It is important that they listen and try to understand.

ADOLESCENCE, IN ITSELF, IS a difficult time but coupled

with an eating disorder it is an even greater challenge. I hope this chapter has shown you the complexities of eating disorders. There is no absolute panacea for treating such illnesses but over the last number of years that I have been working in this area, each day I come to recognise more and more the need to treat the whole person. Anorexia and bulimia are not just a set of 'walking symptoms'. In therapy, the focus is threefold: firstly, to conquer physical development, secondly, to examine and teach healthy processes of socialisation, and thirdly, to teach normal cognitive development.

In order for therapy to be successful the patient must be motivated towards change. Parents cannot successfully force their young teenagers to come for help. It is imperative to begin with individual therapy and as soon as trust and rapport build up between the therapist and the patient, to begin family therapy. You cannot just treat an individual without attempting to examine family interaction. Otherwise, you may be discharging the patient back into the environment which may have triggered the problem in the first instance. I also try to encourage my patients to attend group therapy, to help them overcome feelings of isolation.

Unlike many forms of breakdown, anorexia and bulimia are conditions that can be resolved in time. However, there is always a risk that the condition can recur at times of extreme stress or loss, e.g., bereavement. Complete treatment programmes usually take about two years. Stage one involves assessment, stage two involves in-patient care (for patients medically at risk) and stage three involves follow-up treatment. Hospital programmes in this country, thankfully, have become more holistic. At St Francis Medical Centre we treat the whole person. The team in our hospital in Mullingar is made up of a psychiatrist, psychologist, dietitian, physiotherapist and four nurse therapists. A small percentage of patients, particularly borderline cases, can make successful recoveries without ever going into hospital, if they attend regularly for therapy and are monitored closely by their GP.

Whether in-patient or out-patient, patients must always play an active role in their own recovery. Once they recognise that anorexia and bulimia are breakdowns of the developmental process, and overcome the denial usually associated with such illnesses, they are already on the road to recovery. Adolescence is a difficult time for all of us, but even more difficult if we are prevented from developing into mature, responsible and independent adults. My philosophy for recovery is based on the following belief: *Mens sano, corporo sano*, a healthy mind is a healthy body.

Further Reading

Fabian L.J., Thompson, J.K., 'Body Image and Eating Disturbance in Young Females', *International Journal of Eating Disorders*, 9, pp. 65–74, 1989.

Johnson, C., O'Connor, M.E., *The Etiology and Treatment of Bulimia Nervosa: A Biopsychosocial Perspective*, Basic Books, New York, 1987.

Wilson, C.P., Hogan, C.C. & Mintz, I.L., *Fear of Being Fat: The Treatment of Anorexia Nervosa and Bulimia*, Jason Aronson, New York, 1983.

PANIC

RICHARD BOOTH

I HAD FLOWN DOZENS of times and was startled when, as I walked towards the boarding gate, I could feel my heart pump and my hands shake. I was finding it difficult to swallow and was breathing very quickly. When I started to get dizzy, I had no idea what was happening but felt I was losing control. I was terrified. I wondered was this a stroke or a heart attack. As the sensations intensified, thoughts of boarding became out of the question. I had to get out. People were gathering around the boarding gate and I had to push back through them. I was so desperate that nothing would have stopped me getting out. When I was free of people I started to run. I got back to my car and could hardly get the keys into the lock. Although it was a hot day, I remember turning the heat on to try and stop the trembling.

Very many people will have experienced intense fear when caught in a dangerous situation. Our fear response, which quickens our reactions, can very often get us out of danger. From threats as varied as oncoming cars to seeing the safety of our children at risk, fear helps us to get away or take action to counter a danger. There are many examples of how it has enabled people to make extraordinary efforts involving speed or strength for short periods of time. However, in the incident described above, there was no danger, or no more than had previously been faced on many occasions. Such an unpredicted alarm is very unsettling and can have far-reaching consequences. The questions that will be addressed here are, what is this phenomenon of unexpected intense fear, whom is it likely to affect, and what steps can be taken to eliminate it?

SOME TWO PEOPLE IN EVERY hundred will experience

serious panics in any year. What they report is a surge of emotion, occurring suddenly and unexpectedly, often when there is apparently no reason to be afraid. It is the unexpected nature of what happens that is particularly unsettling; in the words of one person they just 'come out of a clear blue sky'. Lying in bed at night, getting into a lift, just having arrived at a holiday destination are the sort of surprising times when these intense, rapid changes can first be felt. The most commonly reported physical sensations include:

Difficulty breathing
Sweating
Chest pain
Dizziness
Feelings of unreality
Trembling
Choking
Increased heart rate

Faced with these changes it is all too easy to make an anxious interpretation of what might be happening. Common thoughts are:

I am going to die
I am going to lose control
I am going to go crazy
I am going to faint

In a full-blown panic, breathing becomes quicker (though this is not often realised), and this reduces the amount of carbon dioxide in the lungs and intensifies the bodily changes. These can be taken as providing evidence to back one's worst fears that catastrophe is indeed imminent. With each element fuelling the other, intense fear is reached rapidly and with unforgettable impact.

MANY PEOPLE WHO HAVE a panic attack end up in the emergency department of a general hospital. Though they may be persuaded that they are not in physical danger, this does little to reassure them that they will not panic again. They start to become vigilant, looking for the first sign that another panic attack might be starting. They become acutely sensitive to any change in their breathing or heart rate, worrying about what this might herald. Some battle on regardless, with little thought of what might trigger an attack, sometimes with astounding results. I vividly recall the account of one woman who realised only after she had inserted her coins in a car-wash that this was likely to trigger a panic. As her breathing quickened, she felt a desperate need for more air and so rolled down her window. This still seemed insufficient and so she jumped out of the car and hid out of sight of the motorists behind. When she got back in the car she drove off, trying to look calm and hoping that nobody would guess that she was sitting in two feet of soapy water.

Though attacks continue unpredictably, it is common for people to learn that certain situations are more likely to set off an attack. They begin a pattern of avoidance which may easily spread. They also find that they feel safer in one place, or perhaps in the company of one person. Perhaps they take to carrying around an old bottle of medication 'just in case'. In a short time, the effects can be drastic as they fear panic in an ever-increasing number of situations. Seven weeks after her first panic one woman was reduced to driving her husband to work and then waiting for him in the car park all day. Unknown to him, she would spend the entire day in the car before driving him home again in the evening. This secrecy and misery continued for many weeks and shows the terror that can be induced from the prospect of having a panic on one's own.

Recent research suggests that occasional panic attacks are relatively common. Most do not cause concern, perhaps because they are not entirely unexpected or a benign explanation is found (a row, too much coffee or whatever). They are unlikely to recur. But if a panic is severe and there is a real sense of danger, worry about possible recurrence sets in. Avoidance may not be limited to places, but may spread to anything that could bring on internal arousal, so that activities as unlikely as drinking coffee or taking exercise may be avoided; even the expression of emotions can come to have unpleasant associations. Distraction, escape or any such strategy to control an imminent panic attack serve to strengthen the belief that if something had not been done, a truly awful outcome would have taken place.

SINCE THE FIRST SIGN of a panic is physical, then those with a more 'jumpy' system are more susceptible to panic. In addition, there needs to be some stressor. A history of trauma or a poor marital relationship have often been associated with panic, but they are no more common than many possible contributory factors. Pregnancy, holidays or life transitions such as moving house, changing job or getting married are often sufficient triggers for a first panic attack.

An interesting fact is that very many more women than men panic. There are several plausible reasons for this. It could be that it is more acceptable for women to express fear and anxiety, or that males have less opportunity to get into cycles of avoidance. Two other avenues are also currently being explored. The first is the possibility that females have wider-ranging endocrinological changes that make them more susceptible to panic. A fourth notion is that the overall numbers with underlying panic may be reasonably equal but that males cope with means other than avoidance, such as alcohol. It does seem that a substantial number of problem drinkers may require attention for an underlying panic disorder.

THERE ARE MANY WAYS of trying to eliminate panic. If stress levels are lowered this can help, but panic attacks may return if the stress increases again. A variety of medications will also bring down anxiety levels and control physiological symptoms, but relapse is quite common when medication is terminated. Withdrawal can lead to 'rebound panics' which can be more intense than any previously experienced. A further factor is that panic is most likely to affect women in the child-bearing years who may favour alternative methods of treatment. The cognitive behavioural approach is often favoured because it has such a low relapse rate and does not require medication. It involves several elements and is outlined below.

The first step in this approach requires the individual to observe and monitor each panic, noting the specific thoughts and sensations that are typically experienced. Exercises which bring on sensations similar to those felt in a panic are then practiced. For example, by hyperventilating (breathing in through your mouth quickly for several minutes) you can produce dizziness and rapid heart rate very similar to that which many people report. By holding your nose and breathing through a straw you can induce the choking sensations that others report. The more you practice, the easier and less unpleasant these exercises become and the more familiar the feelings are when they occur in a panic. These are combined with a series of breathing and relaxation techniques which can both lower physical reactions to stress and help reduce residual tension after an attack.

The central component of the treatment focuses on testing out what it is that one fears might happen. For example, a common thought in a panic is 'I am about to faint'. The therapist would typically draw up two possibilities. The first is that the individual has been fortunate not to faint and would have done so had they not taken some action just in time. An alternative explanation is that the feeling of faintness is caused by the changes in breathing and blood circulation that are part of the system to help us deal with danger. The therapist then provides some information to help work out which explanation is more credible. People are often surprised to learn that blood pressure and heart rate need to drop to cause faintness, since they know that their heart races during a panic. This means that they are actually less likely to faint when anxious than when relaxed. Such information is of some value but tends not to be really believed in a panic. Deeper change only comes about when risks are taken to find out what really could happen during a panic, rather than through what is learned as part of any rational discussion. Fearful thoughts need to be put to the test when anxiety is high.

A story that is used to illustrate the testing of fearful

thoughts is that of the bricklayer's apprentice. On his first day the apprentice is led to believe that the wall they have been building is at a slight angle and needs to be held up while it dries. One of his assigned tasks is to spend each lunchtime holding up whatever section of the wall has been built in the morning. He is not sure if he is being tricked. The longer he presses against the wall, the more he senses that there may be pressure against his fingertips. At some point he must take a risk. The temptation is for him to take his hands away and put them back again quickly but this does not help. To know what is really going on, he must move away from the wall, and even go around the other side and push. In the treatment of panic it is those who take risks of fainting or losing control or going crazy who make the most progress, as such feared outcomes do not materialise.

RESEARCH FROM DIFFERENT COUNTRIES has shown that anxiety takes many different forms in different countries. Some symptoms, for example, are more pronounced than others in certain places and treatment methods vary dramatically. In Chinese cultures, for example, temperature is a common focus and loss of body heat is a strong fear so that sufferers often wear many layers of clothing. Such concerns can only be understood in the context of the traditional Chinese notions of 'yin' and 'yang', and it is not surprising that western pharmacological techniques have not proved as successful there. Though anxiety may be expressed in different ways, it seems that the experience of panic is common to many cultures. In Iran, for example, it is called 'heart distress' and the experience of palpitations and the resulting concern are similar. Other reports from other cultures include that of an Inuit ('Eskimo') who came to an Alaskan health service reporting that he had been having what were clearly panic attacks for a period of over three years. He was finding it increasingly frightening to leave his home. In desperation, he and his wife had undertaken the 50 mile journey to the hospital by snow-mobile. He had no idea what had started the problem and related it to an episode of 'flu.

Just as it is important to build up accounts of panic from

all over the world, so it is important that our understanding becomes increasingly based on sound research. For too long, ideas based on very small samples were put forward with authority. This led to constant changes in what were considered the underlying factors of panic, a confusing state of affairs particularly for those who suffered from the disorder. Initial clinical observations can now be checked with very large numbers of people. For example, though it initially seemed surprising, some people reported that their worst panic experiences were at night. When large numbers were questioned about such attacks, well over a quarter reported that they had nocturnal panics. These were more common early in the night and during periods of slow-wave sleep. Armed with these facts, researchers can then speculate and test out possible explanations. Such sleep is associated with, among other things, reduced heart rate and occasional muscular twitching. This opens up the possibility that these cues are picked up while asleep and either lead people to wake up with a start, or to become concerned about these changes while still waking up. All of us know that even while asleep we can be attentive to some cues (a baby's cry, for example) and not to others, and it will be important to establish to what extent such attentiveness could be extended to internal cues.

Another way to learn about panic has been to strap small heart rate monitors to a person over a twenty-four hour period and so learn about the physiology of a panic attack. Some researchers have also carried out investigations by 'provoking' panic in a research setting. The research participants are all volunteers with a vulnerability to panic who are keen to help in the development of a better understanding of what leads to such attacks. In one study, participants were asked to go for a walk. They wore ear-phones, attached to a small monitor, through which, they were told, they would be able to hear an amplified sound of their own heartbeat. In fact, what they were listening to was a prerecorded tape of someone else's heartbeat which after 15 minutes speeded up dramatically. The question was, would this be a sufficient cue to start a panic? The answer was 'yes'.

This cue alone increased anxiety greatly and in many cases brought on a full-blown attack. People who have never panicked have no such response. Such a study shows that while there are biological elements to a panic, it is the strength of these initial cues and the way that they can be misinterpreted which are the crucial factors in determining whether anxiety turns to panic.

One further approach has been to break up the whole treatment package into distinct elements and see the effect of each. For example, in one study, one group of panickers received only physical techniques such as relaxation, breathing exercises and training to get used to the physical sensations of panic. A second group was given a treatment which focused exclusively on identifying the thoughts that come in the early stages of panic, and worked on ways in which these might best be countered. A third group was encouraged to expose themselves to as many frightening situations as possible. In this way, much was learned of what are the most potent elements and why certain emphases in treatment seem to help certain people.

Current research is focusing on a variety of subjects including: what happens in a first panic that causes some people to fear internal cues more than external cues?; how do cues spread?; what limitations to treatment are there if people insist on holding on to safety signals such as an empty pillbox?; what techniques help people to apply what they know when they are calm in one of their panics? While these finer points are important for both practical and theoretical reasons, the vital development of the last decade is that this form of treatment has improved greatly. Success rates (as measured by no further panics) have jumped from about 50% to something nearer 90%.

PANICS ARE NOT DANGEROUS. They are our response to danger or perceived danger. They are the ancient method by which, when faced with overwhelming danger, automatic responses take over to help us take immediate action. When working correctly, they are part of a vital mechanism for our survival. When there is no danger and we experience such an alarm, the experience can be so terrifying that it leads to all sorts of doubts and further fears. It is a relatively easy anxiety to treat for those who can brace themselves for some risk-taking. The underlying stresses that may be present are likely to remain and so treatment is not a panacea for all ills. But once panics have been eliminated, this leaves more energy and confidence to tackle whatever other issues may be going on in a person's life.

Further Reading

Barlow, D., *Mastery of Your Anxiety and Panic*, Center for Stress and Anxiety Disorders, 1535 Western Avenue, Albany, New York, 12203, (1990).
Wilson, R., *Don't Panic*, Harper & Row, New York, 1986.

SEXUAL PROBLEMS

TOM KELLY

THOUGH SEXUAL WELL-BEING IS difficult to define, people have little difficulty in defining that which constitutes a breakdown of such well-being. In common with all other cultures, heterosexual Irish people value their ability, in appropriate circumstances, to engage in the act of sexual intercourse. An inability to do so is considered problematic and is the primary and most common reason why people consult psychosexual therapists. Next in importance is the frequency with which sexual activity, but not necessarily intercourse, takes place. Following this in importance is the quality of each sexual encounter. Different people use different criteria to judge quality, but common ones include the experience of a considerable degree of pleasure and the achievement of intimacy. Generally speaking, men put a greater emphasis on quantity whereas women put a greater emphasis on quality.

The vast majority of problems which people define as sexual and for which they seek help are those related to loss or lack of sexual appetite or desire, those related to an inability to engage in the act of sexual intercourse and those which interfere with the experiencing of sexual pleasure. Sexual desires and orientations which do not fit in with society's norms may also be seen as problematic and these include homosexuality, transvestism and fetishism. The most common sexual problems presented by men in psychosexual therapy practices are: (i) difficulties getting or maintaining erections [erectile problems], (ii) poor control over timing of orgasm/ejaculation [premature ejaculation], (iii) lack or loss of interest in sex and (iv) difficulty in reaching orgasm in some or all circumstances [retarded ejaculation].

The most common problems presented by women are: (i) an inability to engage in sexual intercourse because of vaginal spasm [vaginismus], (ii) lack or loss of interest in sex [inhibited sexual desire], (iii) difficulty reaching orgasm in some or all sexual situations [anorgasmia] and (iv) difficulties becoming sexually aroused.

LET US LOOK AT EACH of these problems in turn. Erections occur as a result of the interplay of many features. These features are generally common to all men but their relative importance varies form man to man. Generally speaking, for an erection to occur and be maintained a man must experience sexual desire and a high degree of sexual pleasure. Furthermore, there must be a relative absence of factors which inhibit desire and pleasure. Some men have difficulty in recognising which factors are positive and which are negative and consequently have mixed experiences or indeed may constantly experience erectile problems.

This is particularly likely to happen in young men in early heterosexual experiences. At this time, they are learning to identify the relative merits and demerits of different influences and factors. Most young men experiencing initial erectile problems manage eventually to discriminate sufficiently to overcome their problems, but a minority do not. Those least likely to are those who carry a significant handicap into a sexual relationship. Such handicaps might include poor self-esteem, feelings of sexual inadequacy and fear of intimacy.

It is not uncommon for men in long-term relationships to also suffer erectile problems after many years of trouble-free sex. When the cause is not physical (and in men under fifty years of age it is usually not physical) it is usually related to conflict in the relationship, stress or loss of self-esteem. In vulnerable men erectile problems may lead to depression, drug-related problems or emotional and sexual withdrawal. The extent to which partners of men with erectile problems are affected depends, among other things, on the level of their own self-esteem and the quality of the relationship. Occasionally, erectile problems are a man's way of saying that he is no longer interested in a particular relationship or at least in its sexual aspect. Men who are particularly out of touch with their feelings are prone to giving such indirect messages.

PREMATURE EJACULATION IS DEFINED in a number of ways by those sufferers who seek help from psychosexual therapists. The most distressing form seems to be that in which the man ejaculates very early in a sexual encounter and any hope the couple has of engaging in sexual intercourse is sabotaged. A slightly less extreme form is that in which the man ejaculates within seconds of penetration. Some couples define ejaculation as premature when only the man reaches orgasm during sexual intercourse. Whatever particular criteria are used to define it, what most of these men have in common is the feeling that they have little control over the process. This is a very common phenomenon in young men and decreases in incidence with ageing. The development of greater control with ageing seems to be due to a number of factors. One is the learning of methods of self-control with time. Another is the growth of sexual confidence which most people experience in time and another is the increasing openness and intimacy which most long-term relationships facilitate. When the opportunities to explore and experiment with a sexual partner are absent or not availed of, premature ejaculation tends to become a chronic problem. But even long-standing cases are subject to improvement given the right conditions.

An interesting variation of this problem is the situation in which a man experiences premature ejaculation with one partner but not with a concurrent one. This adds weight to the contention that the ability to control ejaculation is to some degree dependent on the nature of the relationship. Partners of men who suffer from premature ejaculation rarely see it as a negative reflection on themselves. The majority are either perplexed by, or resent, the man's preoccupation with what they themselves regard as a trivial problem. Others feel annoyed that the pleasure and intimacy of sexual intercourse is terminated so soon. Yet others regard it as wilful selfishness on the part of the man. Sufferers tend to see themselves as inadequate and compare themselves unfavourably with friends and neighbours. Some attribute the breakdown of a relationship to the problem. Some avoid future relationships for fear of rejection. Long-term sufferers sometimes develop secondary erectile problems. Where a couple are involved in therapy together the therapist encourages a more open, direct form of sexual communication and teaches the couple specific techniques for gaining control over ejaculations. Where a man does not have a current partner, or will not involve his partner in therapy, there is much less likelihood of the successful outcome which is common in couple therapy.

RETARDED EJACULATION IS RELATIVELY uncommon. Some men do not ejaculate/orgasm in response to any means of stimulation, including masturbation. Others cannot reach orgasm during sexual intercourse but can in response to other means of ejaculation. It is said to affect men who have a greater than usual need to be in control, but this is not always clearly the case and is, in any event, difficult to measure. Most therapists see such a small number of cases that it is difficult to draw general conclusions. In the majority of sufferers it is a primary problem, i.e., it has always been present. The man, or more commonly the couple, usually only seek help when a pregnancy is desired. Otherwise, they appear quite content with their sexual relationship, though the female partner sometimes complains that prolonged intercourse causes her discomfort. On average, about half of sufferers who consult psychosexual therapists overcome the problem within six to ten visits provided their partners are also involved in therapy. Therapy tends to have little to offer those who have never ejaculated by any means during waking hours.

LOSS OF INTEREST IN SEX is a problem about which more and more men are consulting psychosexual therapists. Some describe the problem as universal, i.e., nothing triggers their interest. Others describe their lack of interest as only applying to sex with their partner. In the case of the former, the problem is usually related to either a medical condition, stress or depression. In the case of the latter, the problem usually reflects unresolved conflict in the relationship. This conflict is not always obvious and, in such instances, it often

105

eventually becomes apparent that the man harbours deep resentment towards the partner, sometimes going back over many years. The withdrawal from sex is often accompanied by withdrawal from other forms of intimacy. Sexual withdrawal may also follow a betrayal of trust, such as a partner being unfaithful, for example. Few couples seem to worry about occasional and temporary lapses of interest in sex, but where lapses are frequent or prolonged the partner often feels rejected. Where underlying resentment is the main factor in the man's loss of interest in sex he will not usually initiate efforts to remedy the situation. The rejected partner is the one who invariably initiates such efforts. He will usually only join in such efforts when he perceives a threat to other aspects of the relationship which he values. When both still value the relationship and they seek a remedy together, the outcome is usually favourable. Sometimes, a loss of sexual desire can accompany a loss of interest in the relationship.

LOSS OR LACK OF sexual desire appear to be more common in women. However, this is not always considered problematic. Many women who have active and contented sex lives rarely, or never, experience spontaneous sexual desire. Where the partner always takes the sexual initiative, and is happy to do so, this would not be expected to create problems. However, lack or loss of interest can be problematic when it is accompanied by avoidance of sexual activity. Apart from medical reasons, which are relatively uncommon, psychological causes are many and varied. Absence of sexual desire may accompany anxieties and fears related to sexual activity and may serve the purpose of avoiding these. Examples of such fears and anxieties would include fear of being seen as a poor lover, fear of being judged or ridiculed about one's physical appearance, fear of loss of control and its consequences, fear of commitment to a relationship about which one is ambivalent and so on. It may be a way of expressing anger or hostility or may be associated with unresolved anger. In both men and women, loss of sexual desire may be associated with difficulty in being sexual with a loved one. In such instances, the problem comes to light

106

when the partners commit themselves to a sexual relationship, e.g., when they start living together or get married. Many women seek help when they become fearful of the effect the problem is having on their relationship. Partner reactions vary greatly, but the majority of men feel rejected and this can lead to rows and recriminations. In practice, the majority of couples who seek help for such a problem have been together for a considerable period of time. When the problem is not an indication of a lack of interest or commitment to the relationship, there is a good chance of a successful outcome in therapy.

SEXUAL AROUSAL PROBLEMS IN women are a parallel of erectile problems in men. The problems may vary from being total, i.e., the woman never feels sexually aroused in any situation, to an occasional occurrence in situations which she normally finds arousing. As is the case with men, arousal is a function of many factors and when the balance is in favour of negative factors arousal will be curtailed. This problem may be frustrating since the woman is often at a loss as regards understanding what is going on and she consequently regards herself as a freak. Partners with fragile egos may add fuel to the fire by making negative comments. One of the contributing factors to this type of problem is that many Irish people have difficulty in focusing on what gives sexual pleasure and being able to communicate this to a partner.

Partners of a woman with arousal problems often feel responsible for the woman's pleasure and likewise feel responsible for its absence. They often feel they are doing something wrong and sometimes the woman encourages this belief. Self-esteem seems to play a crucial role in one's ability to let go sexually. Negative self-images, especially relating to one's sexuality, can have a powerful inhibitory affect on arousal. In psychosexual therapy for arousal problems attention is particularly paid to pinpointing negative inhibitory factors with a view to their elimination. Another important focus would be on helping the woman to bolster her self-esteem particularly in regard to her sexuality. In the majority of women such an approach will lead to positive gains.

The circumstances in which women will experience orgasm vary greatly from woman to woman and can also vary greatly in a woman's lifetime. Some women never experience orgasm and never consider this a problem. Others who experience orgasm in some circumstances but not in others will consider it problematic. Much depends on one's perception of what is the common experience and one's expectations. Some women seeking help attribute various misfortunes in life, such as the termination of relationships, to their difficulty in reaching orgasm, whereas others just want to experience what sounds like a wonderful feeling. In some women the difficulty is associated with arousal problems, whereas others have no difficulty becoming aroused but cannot quite reach orgasm despite feeling that they come tantalisingly close. Many women, who have no difficulty reaching orgasm by other means of stimulation, never reach orgasm during sexual intercourse.

In such circumstances, a woman seeking therapy would often have been prompted to do so by her partner. Otherwise, she may say that the idea would never have crossed her mind. Many men feel it is a negative reflection on their sexual prowess if a partner does not reach orgasm during sexual intercourse. In our society young girls and women are sent particularly strong messages about the supposed dangers of letting go sexually. These undoubtedly play a major role in many women's fears about letting go sufficiently to reach orgasm. Most women report that the growing self-confidence which accompanies ageing enables them to sexually let go more and more. The help offered by psychosexual therapists focuses on encouraging the woman to discover for herself which forms of stimulation are most pleasurable and arousing and on helping her let go of society's inhibiting messages which she has internalised.

VAGINISMUS – SPASM OF THE muscles near the entrance to the vagina whenever penetration is attempted – makes sexual intercourse either impossible or extremely painful. It is particularly frustrating because the woman feels she can do nothing to prevent this spasm. It is occasionally caused by physical factors but has a psychological origin in the vast majority of cases. In some women the problem resolves itself spontaneously. A desire to become pregnant is usually what prompts a woman with vaginismus to seek help. This may occur many years after marriage and, in the meantime, the couple would usually have enjoyed an active sex life provided attempts at penetration were avoided. Many sufferers report that they suspected that all might not be well before their first attempt at sexual intercourse. This might have been because they were conscious of an aversion to touching their vulva or vagina, had difficulty inserting tampons, had particular fears about childbirth or experienced fear and disgust at the thought of penile penetration. Some women with vaginismus have a particular difficulty leaving home in the emotional sense. Partners are often conspicuously patient and seemingly unperturbed. They often share the woman's aversion to touching the genitals. However, whatever the particular circumstances may be, the vast majority of women can overcome the problem within a few months of starting therapy.

From the preceding paragraphs it can be seen that the way we classify and describe sexual problems does not do justice to the diversity of human experience and to our relative ignorance about human sexuality. Though we classify certain sexual 'symptoms' as problems, for many people these 'symptoms' are not seen as problems. When two or more people describe their sexual problem in the same way, this does not necessarily mean that they share a common cause or common causes or that they will follow the same path in overcoming the problem. We are still quite ignorant when it comes to knowing what makes people tick sexually. Despite this, a significant proportion of people who consult psychosexual therapists do overcome their problems.

NO STUDIES HAVE BEEN carried out in Ireland to determine what proportion of adults suffers from particular sexual problems. However, we do have results of research carried out in particular settings which give some indication of the prevalence of particular problems. A paper presented to the International Conference of Psychosexual Obstetrics and Gynaecology, at Trinity College, Dublin, by Dr Tom Kelly in 1983 entitled 'Four years experience of treating sexual dysfunction in an Irish family planning clinic', found that erectile problems were the most common concern of men attending the clinic. This was followed by premature ejaculation, then retarded ejaculation. At that time, a small number complained of lack or loss of sexual desire and anorgasmia was an infrequent complaint. Seventy per cent of clients were travelling more than twenty miles to attend the clinic, some up to two hundred miles. In terms of symptom relief, the following were the success rates obtained: Erectile problems, primary (always a problem) – 40%, secondary – 70%; premature ejaculation – 65%; retarded ejaculation – 50%; and loss of sexual desire in men – 60%. Vaginismus – 80%; arousal problems – 80%; loss of sexual desire in women – 60%; and anorgasmia – 40%. Both couples and individuals treated on their own were included in this study.

The findings of the CMAC *Sex Therapy Survey* of 1992 were presented at the BASMT Regional Conference in Dublin in 1992.[1] This survey found the following frequency of problems diagnosed: Men – premature ejaculation – 11%; erectile failure – 10%; and retarded ejaculation – 2%. For women – vaginismus – 34%; anorgasmia – 7%; and painful intercourse – 4%. 32% of clients, male and female, were diagnosed as suffering from inhibited sexual desire. The following headings were used to describe the outcome of therapy: inhibited sexual desire – 46% improvement, 20% total success; erectile failure – 51% improvement, 28% total success; premature ejaculation – 29% improvement, 57% total success; vaginismus – 22% improvement, 68% total success; painful intercourse – 57% improvement, 26% total success;

---

1 *Sex Therapy Survey, 1992*, Catholic Marriage Advisory Council, summary of findings presented to the British Association of Sexual and Marital Therapists, Regional Conference, Dublin, September, 1992.

anorgasmia – 60% improvement. This survey referred to the treatment of couples only.

We have no idea of the number of people who suffer sexual problems and cope with them without the help of professionals, but the number must be considerable. How we perceive changes in our sexual functioning will very much influence our reactions to them and whether or not we consider professional help appropriate. Many factors influence our perceptions of sex and, as a result, we have considerable diversity of opinion as to what constitutes a sexual problem. However, there also appears to be considerable uniformity of opinion as reflected in the ever-increasing number of people who consult therapists with the same sexual problems. For heterosexual men and women in our culture the desire and ability to engage in the act of sexual intercourse with a sexual partner seems to be of fundamental importance. When problems arise in this area most couples are initially loath to involve a third party. Many couples successfully use their own resources to deal with problems that arise. Others struggle for years before turning to others for help. When the decision to seek help is taken, who does one turn to and what type of treatment might one expect?

PETER KIERAN'S STUDY ENTITLED *Psychosexual Counselling and Sex Therapy in the Republic of Ireland,* was the first comprehensive review of these services in Ireland.[2] From the results of his study it seems that the majority of those who are referred to therapists are referred by doctors. However, a significant number of people refer themselves directly. Presumably, doctors have some knowledge of the competence and reputation of those therapists to whom they refer patients, whereas those who refer themselves are presumably much less aware. This is of some importance because Kieran's study also found that 40% of those practising sex therapy and psychosexual counselling, who responded to

2 Kieran, Peter, *Psychosexual Counselling and Sex Therapy in the Republic of Ireland,* unpublished thesis for Masters Degree in Counselling, University College, Cork, 1992.

the study, had no specific training in dealing with sexual problems. There are no statutory regulations regarding who may or may not set themselves up as a sex therapist. The traditional reliance in Ireland on word of mouth rarely applies when people are seeking help with sexual problems. So, overall, choosing a therapist can be a 'hit and miss' affair. Respondents to Kieran's study used a wide variety of titles to describe their work. These included: psychosexual therapist, sex therapist, psychosexual counsellor, sexual counsellor.

Those practising in Ireland whose training and experience satisfy the criteria for membership of the British Association of Sexual and Marital Therapists tend to use similar therapeutic approaches. Broadly speaking, those would include the following. An initial assessment is carried out. This is a two-way affair in which the therapist assesses the likelihood of therapy benefiting the couple or individual and they, in turn, make an assessment of the therapist and any proposed therapy. The relationship is confidential in the same way as is the doctor–patient relationship. If a decision to proceed with therapy is agreed, meetings usually take place on a weekly or fortnightly basis.

The initial meetings are devoted to helping people clarify, in a sexual sense, where they have come from, where they are at and where they want to be. For some people this process alone is sufficient to help them resolve their difficulties. For those who continue the process, specific homework assignments are then introduced. The type of assignment depends on their particular problem. For example, men with premature ejaculation would be given specific exercises to do at home, either alone or with a partner, which would help them to gain greater control over ejaculation. Intervening meetings are used to assess progress and to deal with issues which are hindering progress. When appropriate, people then move on to the next exercise stage.

This type of therapy works best for couples and, indeed, the homework assignments were originally conceived for use by couples. However, many individuals also consult therapists. They may have no current partner or may not wish to involve their partner in therapy. Otherwise, the partner may not wish to be involved. Some of the therapeutic approaches used with couples work just as well with individuals. Where they do not, therapists would rely more on 'talking therapy'. Many therapists are skilled in both approaches.

Most studies on the results of treatment focus on relief of specific sexual symptoms, for example, vaginismus. However, many individuals and couples judge the success of therapy by other criteria. For example, therapy may help partners, who have been wishing to do so, to separate. Sometimes too, in the course of therapy, a couple decides that a particular problem is not too important after all. On occasion too, a couple or an individual may come to realise that they were using a sexual problem as a scapegoat for other problems. Then they can move on to deal with the more important issue or issues. So, broadly speaking, psychosexual therapy is not only about treating sexual symptoms but also about helping people with sexual concerns.

Further Reading

Valins, L., *When a Woman's Body Says No to Sex: Understanding and Overcoming Vaginismus*, Viking Penguin, New York, 1992.
Zilbergeld, B., *Men and Sex*, Fontana/Collins, Glasgow, 1980.
Hooper, A., *The Ultimate Sex Guide*, Dorling Kindersley, London, 1992.

THE ADDICTIONS

ANDREW HONEYMAN

> ... *Whereas in the beginning the difficulty had been to throw off the body of Jekyll, it had of late gradually but decidedly transferred itself to the other side ... I was slowly losing hold of my original and better self and becoming slowly incorporated with my second and worse self ...*
>
> (from DR JEKYLL AND MR HYDE).

Addiction is one of the most stress-producing problems of all and people can only take so much stress before their lives and personalities begin to break down. There is a point when a person emotionally, mentally, spiritually and physically breaks down under the stress and pain produced by an addiction. However, as many can testify, it does not all happen at once – it is a process which occurs slowly and insidiously over time.

Also, although there are many kinds of addictions, (e.g., alcohol, tranquillisers, other drugs, gambling, food, sex, etc), no matter what the addiction is, every addict engages in a relationship with an object or an event in order to produce a desired mood change, an altered state of awareness, and so its origins are rooted in the feelings or in the emotional domain. We must, therefore, understand what all addictions and the process of all addictions have in common – the out of control and aimless searching for wholeness, happiness and peace through a relationship with an object or event. Obviously, true happiness can never be found in this manner, but, nonetheless, this is the false, seductive promise provided by an addiction.

Furthermore, while one may turn to an addictive substance or activity in an attempt to cope with stress, modern living, difficult emotions, an unstable home or social environment – this can then become a problem and indeed a serious one in its own right. When an addiction becomes established, as we shall see, it produces its own symptoms and superimposes its own dysfunction. Thus, problems are created (and maintained) in their own right aside from, and right along with, what may have gone on before.

GIVEN OUR PRESENT STATE of knowledge, we no longer believe that there is one single cause of an established alcohol, drug or gambling problem. Current thinking suggests that a problem of this type emerges as a result of a combination of factors, such as availability, the individual's constitutional make-up, their personality, background, life circumstances and so forth. The issue is complex rather than simple and is best viewed from a multi-factorial perspective.

The truth is that we really do not know why one person gets caught up in an addictive process and another not. However, some may be more susceptible. For example, we know that addiction runs in families – there is an evident 're-generational pattern' attached to it. This may well be 'learned', and in some cases there may be a 'biological' aspect which acts as a predisposing factor. A case in point is the postulated endorphin theory in regard to compulsive gambling. It has been speculated that individuals born with low levels of endorphins (naturally occurring pleasure chemicals that we all have) may be more prone to seek out and engage in activities that increase arousal and excitement, that raise the level of endorphins – for instance gambling. Similarly, a biological determinant – the presence of tetrahydroisoquinilines found in the brains of some alcoholics – has led some researchers to conclude that it is an abnormal brain chemistry that marks alcoholics off from other drinkers, and that it is this which forms the basis of their obsessive drinking. According to others, this abnormal brain chemistry is also formed when an addict shoots heroin into his or her body. As a biological basis for eating disorders it is also claimed that an inherited brain chemistry peculiar to food addiction is at the root of problems with food, specifically an abnormality of the endorphin–enkephalin metabolism.

In relation to these findings it is important to note two things. First of all, such discoveries do not change anything

115

directly for a person recovering from an addiction. Secondly, even in cases where there may be an inherited predisposition, this does not necessarily imply its manifestation. Parental influence, learning, environmental and cultural factors play a large and often underestimated role in shaping one's life. For example, at Rutland Centre about half the people treated have a history of parental addiction.

Furthermore, it seems reasonable to assume that people who lack the skills, or who do not know how to have healthy relationships and have been taught not to trust people, may be more susceptible to the development of an addiction in which one relates primarily to an object or an event. Similarly, if one is raised in a family where there is never any sense of closeness, such a person may be more prone to forming an addictive relationship because he/she is taught to avoid closeness, to keep a distance from others instead of being taught to connect with people. Also, growing up in this type of atmosphere or family may leave one with a deep, lonely emptiness that wants to be filled. An addiction may offer the illusion of this fulfilment. However, it is always only an illusion, as we can never be fully 'complete', in the sense that we will all have anxiety as a normal part of living, along with various insecurities and doubts. How we deal and cope with these is what is important in the long-run, and not their existence *per se*.

The point is that anything which makes us feel good or better than we may have otherwise felt can become the object of our desire and the focus of our attention. We may become preoccupied with it or obsessed by it – developing a sick, dependent relationship with it. This is the pivotal manifestation of what we term the addictive process, essentially when one relates in a dysfunctional, unhealthy way and becomes hooked on this way of relating in order to feel good, at least in the short-term. Therefore, the nature of addiction lies with the type of relationship one has with his or her activity and with its potential to shift the individual's mood in a welcome direction.

Indeed, at one level, the foundation of an addictive personality is found in all of us. It is found in the normal desire

116

to make it through life with the least amount of pain and the greatest amount of pleasure. However, it's when these beliefs control one's way of life, as it does in addiction, that people get into trouble.

Until relatively recently, addictions to alcohol, gambling and drugs were seen as rather separate and discrete entities requiring specific, unique and separate treatments. Now we are seeing the similarities or commonality among the various addictions and that the addictive process is the stem from which the various manifestations take their shape. The addictive process occurs in stages, over time, whereby a given individual comes to rely or depend on a dysfunctional way of being, of relating to others and the world in general. It is chiefly defined by 'an unhealthy dependent relationship'. This can be with some object like alcohol, drugs or food but it can equally refer to sick relationships with people or an activity like gambling or sex. It is dysfunctional in so far as the person concerned has developed a way of behaving and thinking that is self-defeating, yet persists in it.

IN OUR COUNTRY TODAY, the facts are testimony to society's attitude and behaviour in this regard. Over the past year, according to the Central Statistics Office, we spent an estimated £1.8 billion on alcohol alone, i.e., £5.05 million per day. The most recent figures from the Health Research Board indicate that 23% of total admissions to our psychiatric hospitals are for 'alcoholic disorders'. In general, it is estimated that around 11% of men and 3% of women drink sufficiently to excess to cause significant health problems. However, it is very likely that these figures are underestimated, particularly when we consider the current trend of more women drinking and of both sexes drinking at a younger age. In regard to drug abuse, the Health Research Board estimates that nearly 2,000 attended for treatment of one sort or another in Dublin, excluding the rest of the country, over a one year period. More recently (October 1993), the Department of Health estimated that there are now more than 5,000 drug abusers in Dublin. As far as compulsive gambling is concerned, no exact figures are available for Ireland. However, it is

117

estimated in the western world, where the majority of the population gambles, that anywhere from 1.5% to 4% of the adult population may be compulsive gamblers, with as many as one in five being women.

The implications of all this for the people concerned and society in general are far-reaching and it is no wonder that people have begun to question whether or not we are living in an addictive society, looking for a quick-fix solution to life's problems.

IT MAY BE HELPFUL to put the issue under discussion in an overall developmental context. At birth, we are born into the world helpless and totally dependent on others for our survival and well-being. As we grow and develop, ideally in a nurturing climate, we become less dependent and more independent. Evaluating, sorting out, and achieving a balance of dependence/independence, is a life-long process and conflict attached to the human condition. This struggle is not something peculiar only to adolescence and youth. In reality, it is a major life problem for everyone and no one ever really quite makes it. Not surprisingly, 'dependency issues' may arise in one form or another throughout life. An addiction is primarily a dependency or relational issue and needs to be seen in that context to be properly understood and appropriately treated.

Parental responsibility towards a child, among other things, is to help him/her individuate. Individuation is the process of becoming a person in your own right. If the parents have not become individuated themselves, then they inadvertently tend to entangle and enmesh their children in a lack of individuation which, if it goes on unrecognised, is likely to bring its own problems for the child later on. Oftentimes, this lack of individuation may manifest itself in *active addiction* or *co-dependency*. Therefore, in order to describe characteristics of the addictive process, I would like to briefly focus on each of these.

Active addiction, or what is sometimes referred to as 'wet systems', simply refers to the fact that the individual concerned is actively drinking, drugging or gambling or at least does so at regular intervals. As already stated, while there is no clear-cut personality-type which predisposes to addiction, there is evidence that a cluster of personality traits becomes identifiable amongst those with an established alcohol, drug or gambling dependency. First of all, the true start of any addictive relationship is when the person repeatedly seeks the illusion of relief to avoid unpleasant feelings or situations, thus fostering a psychological dependency or what becomes an 'irrational' need to drink, drug or gamble (or to engage in the respective addictive activity) in spite of the consequences.

So there tends to be a loss of choice and balance in regard to the addictive activity. This is another key element, referred to as reduced or impaired control, reflected by the fact that individuals cannot reliably predict what will happen when they drink, drug, or gamble. In essence, the person cannot handle or deal with the 'action' of gambling or alcohol or drugs on any kind of regular basis. When the person drinks, for example, they may take more than intended and/or their behaviour and the evident mood-swings that go hand in hand with addiction give rise to family members in particular, and others in general, referring to a 'Jekyll and Hyde' type personality. The individual's personality can, and does, change in many instances. A great deal of self-hatred tends to build up as the individual concerned behaves in a way that is in conflict with his or her own values. Eventually, a free-floating mass of negative feelings may develop and this is what contributes significantly to the personality changes. The individual acts out such feelings as anger, resentment, self-hatred and other unresolved issues. These are projected or displaced onto others, usually in a blaming way. He or she may be verbally or physically aggressive or just plain moody. In fact, the addicted persons compromise their own value systems to such an extent that, in order to cope, they may well cut-off emotionally from themselves and others, gradually becoming out of touch, developing low self-esteem and an inadequate sense of their own identity. Remaining detached, they can begin to lose touch with who they are. Over time, the individuals are likely to become so preoccupied with their addiction that it becomes the consuming focus of their thoughts and behaviour.

Mental obsession, emotional compulsion, ritualistic and premeditated behaviour are typical. In this sense, the addiction is allocated a priority status to the neglect of other matters and responsibilities. The person is likely to change his/her lifestyle to facilitate the addiction, use strategies and deceit to get his/her own way and become quite manipulative. Yet, with all this, the addict remains ignorant about the extent of the problem, through denying the reality of the drinking, drugging or gambling itself and the addicted related behaviour. Most notably, this is achieved through repression, making excuses (rationalising), minimising the seriousness of the problem and by the projection of blame. All of these alienate others, and leave the individual with strong feelings of isolation.

A sense of futility, despair and hopelessness can reach such proportions that the individual's thoughts may turn to suicide as an option, as the only way out of what has become a vicious circle. The addiction has created the very thing the person is trying desperately to avoid – pain. In order to avoid breaking down completely it is inevitable that various defences will be used, primarily to protect self-esteem, but they also protect and lock-in the addictive process. Even with defences, 'suppressed conflict' may seep through to consciousness in the form of diffuse feelings, vague fears and ill-defined anxieties, conveying that all is not well in the psyche.

For those abusing alcohol or drugs, the lack of awareness is compounded by amnesic episodes or blackouts, during which the person apparently functions normally but cannot subsequently recall details of behaviour. These occur for some on a regular basis. It can be very embarrassing if the person concerned cannot remember what they did or indeed where they were, and may lead them to become unusually suspicious. Often combining with blackouts is 'euphoric recall' which serves to boost denial, as it relates to recalling aspects of the addiction in a pleasant or euphoric way despite adverse consequences in reality. For example, the compulsive gambler may recall the wins he or she had, forgetting about the losses and debts or become incurably and irrationally optimistic about the next big win.

Again, where chemicals are concerned, at a physical level there is often 'elevated tolerance' where the person can consume quantities or amounts of alcohol/drugs that would be poisonous for the non-drinker/drug-taker. As time goes on, however, this tolerance may fluctuate as the person's liver, brain and other organs become impaired. Addiction takes its toll physically, not only directly from the effects of chemical usage but also due to the mounting stress the person is under.

This may manifest itself in the form of high blood-pressure, stomach upsets, ulcers, backache, headache, general tension and all sorts of psychosomatic problems. These then, are just some, but I feel the main, symptoms of active addiction.

Co-dependency: there are two main reasons for referring to co-dependency. The first is the increasing awareness among professionals in the field that beneath the surface of active addiction more often than not are co-dependency issues. Secondly, people who live with, or close to, a dependent person are likely to have become co-dependents themselves to a greater or lesser extent.

The term 'co-dependency' itself is, I feel, a little unfortunate, despite its role in opening 'doors of healing' for many. The reason I say this is that it suggests the notion of 'not as bad as' or 'superior to' addicts. Furthermore, it encourages the adoption of a 'victim' stance on the part of the family members who can somehow justify their own behaviour on these grounds. Most important of all is that the co-dependent individual is defined, and defines himself/herself, not as a person but rather in terms of the relationship they have with another person, namely the addicted individual. Their selfhood and self-responsibility are therefore being denied. Ironically, one of the most central aspects of co-dependency – being externally referenced – is actually being reinforced by the very term itself.

Co-dependency is, to a greater or lesser extent, where a person has failed to 'individuate' and so has 'emotional gaps' in his/her own personal development and may look towards others to fill these, which of course they never can. It is usually observed in one's manner of relating and in the type of relationships established. It's also about being addicted to dysfunction. This may be evident prior to active addiction or it may develop as a response to it.

If one is living in an unhealthy or abnormal situation then, generally speaking, there are two choices. One either confronts the issue or situation in some way (even if this is only within oneself) or else one 'adapts' to it which means developing unhealthy patterns. For example, in order to cope with addiction, family members often develop styles, ways of coping, or ways of behaving and thinking that enable such an adaptation to an abnormal situation to take place. They get caught in the 'family trap' of enabling.

Enabling: family members inevitably become affected, as they get sucked into the addictive process themselves. In their attempt to cope with the problem they may inadvertently 'enable'. This is any behaviour by family members or friends which aims to contain or limit drinking, drug-taking or gambling, or to shield the dependent person from the familial, legal, social or work-related implications of his/her ongoing excesses. Although based on a desire to resolve problems, 'enabling' actually worsens the situation in the long-run by (i) removing responsibility from the person whose drinking, drug-taking or gambling is creating difficulties and (ii) thereby slowing-down recognition of the problem in the dependent person. People do it because it initially seems the right thing to do – to protect those we love. It is well-intentioned, yet tragically plays a destructive role in helping to arrest the ongoing dependency.

External referenting: this is central to the addictive process. It means that one believes and acts as though meaning and self-worth come from outside – that the reference point for thinking, feeling and doing is external to the self, rather than knowing what one thinks and feels from the inside and then relating to the world from that perspective. In active addiction one turns to alcohol, drugs or gambling. When not active, one may turn to people, objects or other events in this externally directed way. Some issues follow from this. Since the individual feels that he/she has no intrinsic meaning of his/her own, whatever small vestige of self does exist is easily given away in order to maintain a relationship, because the individual may feel like literally nothing without the relationship. It may be the type of relationship where both parties feel they cannot survive without the other, a condition that provides the relationship with security. The kind of security, however, which will be bought at any cost is static and non-growing. A great deal of energy can be put into keeping such a relationship together, often at great personal cost. Being overly-dependent on others' approval or opinions can also be a feature. The person may become obsessed with managing impressions – controlling others' perception of them to the exclusion of their own needs. As a result, one denies the reality of one's own feelings/experiences which, in turn, become frozen or repressed. This, of course, brings its own level of stress and emotional, mental and physical symptoms which at the end of the day can lead to breakdown.

Cross-Addictions: individuals who may give up one addiction and yet not tackle the underlying issues may continue to be externally referented. Thus the object of obsession may be transferred, for example, from alcohol to tranquillisers or from gambling to alcohol. There can be 'switched addictions', and indeed it seems that people are most vulnerable to developing a second addiction when recovering from a first. Perhaps the transference may not be onto a chemical at all but instead onto a relationship, food, sex or work – to name a few possible substitutions. This is why, when we speak of abstinence in the real sense, we are talking about the recovering individuals being very clear and specific and totally honest with themselves and others when deciding what is addictive behaviour for them. The persons then need to commit themselves to abstaining from these very behaviours and rituals and not merely abstain from a chemical or the 'action' of gambling.

123

TREATMENT AND RECOVERY: PEOPLE, whether they are addicted or not, are different from one another, having their own individual uniqueness in relation to life experiences. It follows that, in treatment, individuals have different starting points. For example, some have a reasonably uncomplicated history with no prior pathology, while others may have been wounded by traumatic blows early in life or have significant inadequacies which predate their active addiction. Therefore, there may be a need for individuals to look at the past to learn more about themselves. This carries challenges with it – *knowing* about the past is not enough. On the contrary, many people can get stuck when they realise that there are reasons why they behave the way they do or feel the way they do. People can become hooked onto their victim status, become immobilised, frozen with such feelings as sadness and anger. Insight, while very important, is only one side of the therapeutic coin. Having understood, we need to learn how to move on, to act differently. This is the promise of recovery.

The central perspective of recovery is personal growth – restoring mental, emotional, spiritual and physical health. It is about being abstinent, tackling the underlying problems, the many self-defeating behaviours that have developed as a result of the addiction and those that have even predated it. It is about making relationships work which may have been stagnant for years. Most of all, it is about having a good quality of life.

Each person, of course, makes progress in his/her own unique way, and change, for the most part, is wavy and unpredictable – it does not occur in a straight line. Various 'fellowships' have developed over the years, originating with the founding of Alcoholics Anonymous in 1935. Since then, self-help groups have expanded and developed into dealing with other addictions, and are an invaluable source of support to those suffering in this regard.

Of course, the first step is to admit that there is a problem. By becoming non-enabling and/or conducting an intervention, family members can help the dependent person to recognise the problem and increase motivation for help.

Whatever the situation, remember not to try and fight the battle by yourself, whether you are a family member or an individual with a problem. There is support available and no addiction is ever a 'do it yourself' job.

Recovery rates, no matter how they are defined, vary dramatically from facility to facility, with the 'average' success rate being put at about 31%, testifying to the difficulty and challenge posed by such a condition. However, it is important to avoid the extremely naive positions – firstly, that all treatments have equal value and, secondly, the embittered stance that none works at all.

Treatments which focus only on eliminating the 'abuse' are less successful than those which emphasise the acquisition of coping skills, modification of lifestyle, and facilitate the reintegration with family and/or community. Furthermore, programmes which harness the 'social supports' and offer a continuum of care, markedly enhance remission and outcome rates, with reported success of between 70% and 80%. This bodes well for the future and offers hope to those who may have believed their situation to be hopeless.

Alongside this hope, we must recognise that there are no 'instant solutions' and that growth is always a gradual process, a bridge slowly crossed and not a corner sharply turned.

Further Reading

Johnson, V., *I'll Quit Tomorrow*, Harper & Row, San Francisco, 1990.

Ditzler, J. & Ditzler, J., *Coming Off Drink*, Papermac, London, 1987.

Ward, Y., *A Bottle in the Cupboard: Women and Alcohol*, Attic Press, Dublin, 1993.

Ditzler, J., Ditzler, J. & Haddon, C., *Coming Off Drugs*, Papermac, London, 1986.

Neild, L., *Escape from Tranquillisers and Sleeping Pills*, Ebury Press, London, 1990.

Custer, R. & Milt, H., *When Luck Runs Out. Help for Compulsive Gamblers and their Families*, Facts on File Publication, New York, 1985.

Beattie, M., *Beyond Co-Dependency*, Hazelden, New York, 1989.

Sheppard, K., *Food Addiction The Body Knows*, Health Communications Inc., Deerfield Beach, Florida, 1989.

PHOBIAS

MARY MCGOLDRICK

THE WORD 'FEAR' COMES from the old English 'faer' for sudden calamity or danger. Fear can be defined as the usually unpleasant feeling that arises as a normal response to realistic danger. It is a vital legacy from our evolutionary past which leads us to avoid threat and has obvious survival value. It is the emotion produced by the perception of present or impending danger and is normal in appropriate situations. Fear in its less extreme form can be not only useful but also enjoyable. Many people enjoy mastering danger in sports such as mountaineering or car-racing. However, in the absence of any obvious threat, feelings of fear can become incapacitating and disabling, affecting many aspects of our daily lives.

Most children and adults have minor fears of one kind or another. Children are afraid of their parents leaving them, unusual noises and strangers. Adults, on the other hand, can be frightened by heights, spiders and speaking in front of large audiences. However, these minor fears do not lead to total avoidance of these situations nor do they significantly interfere with the quality of the lives of those concerned. A listening ear may be all that is required to alleviate these fears.

The word anxiety comes from the Latin word 'anxius', meaning a condition of agitation and distress. It is an emotion akin to fear but it can be distinguished from fear in a number of ways. When you are afraid, your fear is usually directed towards some concrete, external object or situation. The event that you fear usually is within the bounds of possibility. You might, for instance, fear failing an exam or being rejected by somebody you want to please. When you experience anxiety, on the other hand, you often cannot specify what it is you are anxious about. The focus of anxiety is internal rather than external. It seems to be a response to a vague or even unrecognised danger. You might well be anxious about 'losing control' of yourself or some situation.

Anxiety is an inevitable part of modern everyday life. There are many everyday situations in which it is appropriate and reasonable to experience some degree of anxiety. It is only when this anxiety increases in intensity, frequency and duration that it becomes problematic.

A PHOBIA CAN BE defined as a fear of a situation that is out of proportion to its danger, can neither be explained nor reasoned away, is largely beyond voluntary control and leads to avoidance of the feared situation (Marks, 1978). Phobias can occur in almost any situation and researchers have identified more than three hundred different phobias. Formal names which have been given to some phobias include: arachnophobia – a fear of spiders; pyrophobia – a fear of fire; trichophobia – a fear of hair and brontophobia – a fear of thunder.

There are three general categories of phobias – simple phobias, agoraphobia and social phobia. Simple phobias may develop gradually out of childhood fears and social phobias most commonly have their onset in late adolescence. Agoraphobia appears to start most frequently either in late adolescence or about the age of thirty. It is difficult to calculate the frequency of phobias in the population as a whole because there is no hard and fast distinction between 'normal fears' and phobias and because people tend to be reticent about disclosing their fears. Nevertheless, mild phobias are thought to be common in early childhood, disappearing for the most part by the age of six.

In adults, phobias are slightly more common in females than in males. It is estimated that about 80% of agoraphobics are women while the sexes are equally divided in social phobia. About 60% of the phobic patients seen in an outpatient clinic are agoraphobics and social phobics form the next largest group. Although the exact cause of phobias is not known, they are generally considered to be learned fears, arising perhaps from some negative experience or from hearing somebody express extreme anxiety in a similar situation. It is, however, unusual for a phobic patient to describe a single traumatic event, such as being bitten, to which he/she can date the exact onset of the phobia. Fear generally builds up gradually, as a result of repeated, frightening experiences or through social learning. This can happen at a time of stress when arousal levels are high and fear responses are easily learned.

People can respond to something they fear in a variety of ways. These responses can be classified under three headings: physiological, behavioural and subjective. If, for example, you just missed being knocked down by a bus as you crossed a busy road, then you might complain of sweating, shaking, a rapid heartbeat, 'jelly legs', 'butterflies' in the stomach. You might scream, run away or freeze and you certainly would have some thoughts and feelings about the incident. In this case the symptoms of fear would quickly die away and the experience itself might be useful from the point of view of making you more careful crossing busy roads in future. This reaction would not be useful if it was provoked by something that was not really dangerous, e.g., a spider.

THREE CHARACTERISTICS WHICH DISTINGUISH a phobia from ordinary everyday fears are: (i) the persistent fear of the object or situation over a long period of time; (ii) although you know your fear is unreasonable, this does not help to dispel it and (iii) avoidance of the feared object or situation. By definition, phobic fear is disproportional to the source of the danger and reactions such as carefulness and avoidance in situations provoking such fear are inappropriate.

The more common and familiar the phobic object, the greater the incomprehension and lack of sympathy which the phobic encounters in normal people. Most people have difficulty understanding how anybody could be scared of a playful dog or being alone in one's home. It is difficult for the average person in the street to comprehend the intensity of feeling and handicap caused by phobias. The apparent lack of understanding on the part of some people makes many phobics sensitive and ashamed of their fears. They are afraid of being ridiculed by others for having these fears and so hide their fears and suffer in silence.

A specific phobia is characterised by a persistent and irrational fear of a specific object or a specific situation. The person concerned may have a compelling desire to avoid the object or situation in question and this may cause considerable inconvenience. When the person involved is exposed to the feared object or situation, a reaction of fear will follow almost immediately. The fear is not of having a panic attack (as in agoraphobia) or of humiliation (as in social phobia). The person in question realises that the fear is disproportional and irrational. In clinical practice the commonest fears are those of spiders, mice, cats, dogs, bees and wasps. Most animal phobics expect, on meeting their feared animal, to panic, go insane, have a heart attack, be acutely embarrassed or accidentally injured while fleeing from it. Only a few believe the animal will hurt them. Fears of animals are normal developmental features of childhood which arise between the ages of two and four and then subside. Fears of blood or injury, heights, thunder and flying are somewhat less common.

For some, these fears may be more of a nuisance than a disability. For others, however, contact with the feared object may induce striking distress, panic, sweating and trembling. Only a minority of people with simple phobias actually seek treatment. The reason for this may be the fact that they are so embarrassed about disclosing the nature of their fear or indeed have structured their lives in such a way as to minimise exposure to the feared object or situation. Treatment may be sought when a person's living conditions change so that confrontation with the awe-inspiring situation becomes more frequent and their lives become restricted as a result of their fears. Women often come for treatment because they fear transmitting their phobia to their children.

For blood/injury phobics the mere sight of blood or physical injury can arouse feelings of uneasiness not to mention nausea. Blood phobias can be found in about 2–3% of the 'normal' population and feature as one of the most prominent phobias in adults. Blood phobias differ remarkably from other simple phobias. Of particular note is the fact that, at the sight or the mention of blood or injury, these individuals may experience a slight rise in heart rate and blood pressure. However, within a short period of time, this is followed by a slowing down of the heart rate with a drop in blood pressure accompanied by nausea, sweating, pallor and the person may faint.

THE TERM 'AGORAPHOBIA' WAS first used by Westphal (1871) although the condition itself had been observed for some time prior to this. He used the term to describe complete avoidance of walking through certain streets or squares, or extreme dread of anxiety when doing so. The word itself comes from the Greek 'agora' meaning place of assembly and 'phobos' meaning terror or fright. An essential feature of the condition is the marked fear of being alone or being in public places from which escape might be difficult or help not available in case of a sudden incapacitation. It describes varying combinations of fears of going into stores, standing in queues, crowds and public places, travelling on trains, buses, planes and cars, being in a traffic jam, entering closed areas such as elevators, churches, theatres, crossing bridges, having a haircut and leaving or staying at home alone. It leads people to avoid these areas because they are afraid of bringing on the symptoms of panic and they may also fear having a heart attack, a stroke or losing control, screaming or going insane.

Most agoraphobics are more fearful when alone. They often avoid being alone and feel less anxious when accompanied by a trusted person, for example a partner or a person who is aware of their problem. However, not all agoraphobics feel comfortable in company. A number of them report feeling anxious when they are accompanied, because being in company may make their escape more difficult. For some agoraphobics the presence of young children appears to be an additional source of worry instead of being a comfort. They may also experience great anticipatory anxiety before entering what they consider a potentially frightening situation. In an effort to minimise feeling trapped in situations, individuals often shop at quiet times, drive on minor roads as opposed to major roads, and sit near an exit in the church, cinema and theatre. Pushing a pram, carrying an umbrella or money can affect the levels of anxiety experienced in any of these situations.

Agoraphobia often follows a predictable pattern. For most, the condition usually follows a period of 'stress' and the experience of a 'panic attack'. In some instances a series of panic attacks can occur before avoidance behaviour sets in. Panic attacks are discrete periods of intense fear or discomfort often occuring unexpectedly. Because panic attacks are so unpleasant and frightening the individual begins to fear their recurrence. This 'anticipatory anxiety' can often precipitate the very thing feared. The individual starts to avoid places where panic was first experienced and then gradually avoids new situations for fear that these too might precipitate further panic. Gradually, he/she fears more and more places and movement becomes curtailed and restricted.

The condition varies in severity. In some people the pattern of avoidance does not develop to any significant degree and to cope they merely grit their teeth and ride through the panic without curtailing their activities. This may result in exhaustion, as everyday activity is overlaid by continual, wearing anxiety. For others, avoidance allows them to remain relatively panic-free. Their lifestyle becomes restricted and they may become bored, frustrated or depressed. However, this way of coping can keep panic and anxiety to a minimum. For some, both panic and avoidance become part of their everyday life, interfering with their work, their home, their personal and also their social lives.

Agoraphobia is an extremely common condition. It affects people from all walks of life and at all levels of the socio-economic scale. It is estimated that 50% to 80% of all phobics are agoraphobic. In fact, 6 out of 1,000 of the population are agoraphobic. Approximately 80% of agoraphobics are women, although this percentage has been dropping recently. Typically, the onset of the condition occurs between the ages of sixteen and forty and individuals become disabled by their symptoms 15 months after onset. It may develop after some major upheaval or life event such as a serious illness, bereavement, pregnancy or marriage. In the past, people have tended to wait between 10 and 13 years from the onset of their difficulties before seeking help.

SOCIAL FEARS ARE COMMON in the general population. Most of us can remember feeling embarrassed, awkward and insecure at various times in our lives. These feelings generally lessen with time as our confidence and social experience grow. Situations that typically cause some degree of anxiety include public-speaking and dealing with people in authority. Social phobia is a persistent fear of one or more situations in which the individual is exposed to possible scrutiny by others and fears that he/she may do something or act in a way that will be humiliating or embarrassing. Confrontation with the feared situation usually elicits anxiety. These situations, in general, will be avoided or endured only with intense anxiety. People with social phobia report blushing, shaking and sweating, unlike agoraphobics where the predominant physical symptoms are dizziness, palpitations and 'jelly legs'. Although very fearful in certain situations, people with social phobia often do not engage in overt avoidance behaviour, but have more subtle avoidances in their repertoire.

Individuals may be afraid to eat or drink with other people, fearing that their hand may tremble and people may notice this and think poorly of them. For fear of shaking or blushing, some social phobics will not sit opposite another person or walk past a waiting line of people. They are terrified of attracting attention by behaving awkwardly. Some only feel safe leaving their homes at night when they cannot easily be recognised. Writing cheques or signing signatures is another source of worry for some individuals.

Because social phobics often hide their fears, it is difficult to ascertain the level of debilitation associated with the condition. Individuals often underestimate the impact of the condition on their lives. They develop a pattern that protects against experiencing the fear. Avoidance may be subtle and may not be recognised by the individuals as such, because it becomes part of their routine behaviour pattern.

Social phobia is unique among the phobic conditions in that the disorder appears to affect men and women in almost equal proportions. It is estimated to affect about 2% of the general population. Although social phobia can develop at any age, there appears to be a characteristically earlier age of onset than for the other anxiety disorders. Early adolescence seems to be a crucial period for the onset of this condition. This may be because the adolescent years are a time when peer relationships and peer groups take on greater significance and adolescents are confronted with the task of establishing their role and place within a social system other than their family. Some individuals comment that they have always been shy and retiring even from an early age in social situations. Others can recall feeling awkward, embarrassed or 'made fun of' when reading in front of their classmates. Social phobics often use alcohol and medication to alleviate their distress. Social phobia can result in significant emotional, social and occupational impairment.

For people who suffer from any of these phobic conditions, feelings of guilt, hopelessness, helplessness and worthlessness are common. There is guilt at not being able to cope psychologically with something everybody else thinks one should be able to deal with, guilt at being unable to function as a normal parent or spouse, not being able to do the routine things all parents do for their children, and guilt at not being able to go shopping, attend school functions or socialise. There is guilt above all at restricting the lives and opportunities of others. Those who live with or are in close contact with somebody who has a phobia know only too well the restrictions and the effects it can have on their lives as well. Promotional and social opportunities may be lost because of the restrictions. Feelings of anger and resentment can affect the quality of relationships.

When the fear and avoidance yield a level of distress or impairment that becomes intolerable for the individual concerned or his/her partner, then treatment is usually sought.

The individual may become isolated and lonely and these feelings in themselves may then become the impetus for seeking help.

IF YOU THINK YOU have a problem with phobias then the first step is to contact your general practitioner. A medical examination may be necessary to rule out any physical condition which may be contributing to your anxiety. A behavioural self-help approach is worth considering when your problem is not too severe and you feel you may overcome some of the difficulties without professional help. This approach involves helping the phobic individual to face the situations that provoke anxiety in a prolonged graded way. In order to devise a personal programme for graded practice you need to:

1) Make a list of all the situations you avoid or that make you anxious.

2) Arrange this list in order, according to how difficult it would be for you to face each task.

3) Select the easiest task on the list as a first task for practice. This task should be easy enough for you to be reasonably certain you can attempt it, but sufficiently hard to provoke some degree of anxiety.

4) This first task should be practised regularly so that eventually you can complete it without too much anxiety. *Remember the aim is not to abolish anxiety but to teach you to manage it differently in a competent way.*

5) Once you have successfully completed the first task move on to the next item on your list. Practice is useful when it is regular, frequent and prolonged. You need to practice until your anxiety decreases to a more acceptable level. Do not be put off by feeling anxious. Facing situations you have been avoiding is not particularly comfortable or pleasant.

6) Keep an accurate, written record of the practice you carry out. Record the date, the duration of each task and the level of anxiety experienced in each situation. It is not unusual for people working through a list to casti-

gate themselves for not making sufficiently rapid progress.

7) Reward yourself consistently for any achievements no matter how small.

8) Try using some strategies to control your anxiety while it is at a relatively low level. Some phobics find slow deep breathing, relaxation, distraction and positive coping statements useful for this purpose. These techniques need to be practised regularly. Some people find it useful to write a selection of these on postcards and carry them with them while practising. *Regular practice is the key to overcoming these difficulties.*

9) Frequently, people encounter 'setbacks', difficulties in situations they had previously mastered. These are an integral part of progress and it is very important not to let them discourage you from further practice. As long as you continue to practice you will be doing something positive to overcome your anxiety.

If having tried the above suggestions you feel there is little change with regard to your avoidance and anxiety, then ask your general practitioner to refer you to a clinic specialising in the treatment of anxiety disorders. It is not uncommon that severe anxiety symptoms or an underlying depression can inhibit a person's ability to follow such a programme. In these instances medication may be indicated to facilitate treatment. Many psychiatric and some general hospitals employ psychiatrists, psychologists and nurse therapists trained in the field of anxiety management. The greater availability and accessibility of treatment will hopefully result in people referring themselves for treatment earlier. Frequently, it is easier to assist in the early stages, prior to the difficulties becoming an entrenched part of the person's lifestyle. Nevertheless, people with an extended duration of symptoms are also amenable to treatment and they should not refrain from seeking help because they have had and have coped with their problems for a long time.

People who are overcoming their phobias, their partners and their families may need to readjust to the changes that occur as part of getting better. People with phobias often become more assertive and move from being dependent to becoming more independent. Sometimes, relationships need adjusting too to accommodate these changes. Those who helped the patient most during the crippling stages of the condition may now feel cast aside, no longer needed or appreciated. It is necessary for the person overcoming the phobia to be aware of this and to help his/her partner during the transition.

Because all kinds of things that were impossible before now become possible, patients often start formulating new goals for their lives and fulfilling longed-for dreams. As they recover, people still need encouragement, praise and support.

Further Reading
Marks, Isaac, *Living With Fear*, McGraw Hill, New York, 1978.
Zimbardo, Philip, *Shyness*, Pan Books, London, 1977.
Weekes, Claire, *Self-Help For Your Nerves*, Fontana, London, 1992.

ADOLESCENT BREAKDOWN

PAUL ANDREWS

IN THIS CHAPTER WE are talking about something different from the neurotic or psychotic states that may be genetically determined and can occur at any time of life. We are looking at those breaking points which are associated specifically with the teen years and arise out of the tasks of the teens.

Cataloguing possible calamities is a depressing business and can easily mislead one into thinking that growing up is hazardous. Before we start to list the dangers, it is worth stressing that for the great majority of adolescents, health and harmony are the norm.[1] Despite the fact that adolescent crises often occur at a time when the parents are approaching their own mid-life crisis, and are running out of their first enthusiasm to sacrifice everything for their children, four out of five families bring their children through the teens in relative harmony: not conflict-free, but with the capacity to negotiate solutions without undue or prolonged friction. Appreciable psychological stress is found in less than 20% of adolescents, and only one in ten families experiences a dramatic deterioration of relationships between parents and teenage children.

In physical terms, adolescence is perhaps the healthiest and most vigorous period of one's life. But one does meet abnormal responses to the normal stresses of adolescence. The ordinary functioning of the mind or personality has broken down. The human functions which Freud saw as signs of mental health, loving and working, start to falter. Family and friends look on with alarm and speak of a 'nervous breakdown'. Many of the wildnesses that adults dread

---

1*Journal of Child Psychology and Psychiatry*, Vol. 34, No. 1, p. 69, P. Hill, 'Recent advances in selected aspects of adolescent development', Pergamon Press, 1993.

in teenagers are transitory and no medicine will cure them. Time will. But there are similarities to psychiatric conditions. The upset can show itself as a difficulty with living and working. Parents can experience the state of their teenage children as pushing family life to the edge of what is tolerable. They often fear madness and call in a psychiatrist.

BRENDAN WAS A BOY of average intelligence in a family with brains to burn. He was aware and jealous of the achievements of his big brother and sister, and overawed by the attainments of his father, which he read as posing expectations for himself. It was a united family, with tolerant and understanding parents, but Brendan tested and baffled them. At the age of twenty, having sampled eight schools, he was still struggling to pass subjects in the Leaving Certificate when his behaviour became more and more bizarre. He became solitary, stopped going to class, slept through the day and stayed up watching television at night, pulled out his eyelashes, burned many of his own possessions, painted his room black, fought furiously with any of the family who tried to come close to him and refused to see a doctor.

Eventually, his parents contrived, with great difficulty, to have him admitted to a psychiatric hospital for observation. He blossomed there, was a support to staff and patients, and emerged three weeks later certified as free from pathology, but nursing a fierce anger towards the parents who had committed him.

It is hard to fault those parents. They were facing signs of a serious depression. Brendan was mutilating his body, burning his past, painting his room black and shunning the daylight. The depression had the particular flavour of adolescence in his fear of being overwhelmed by his parents and his refusal to talk to them or to a doctor. He wanted to find his own solutions rather than be treated like a child. There were echoes of an old Oedipal tension in his focusing of hatred on his father while he remained open to tenderness from his mother. He turned against her only when she aligned herself with his father, but it was through her warmth that he eventually recovered some balance.

138

IRELAND'S TEENAGE POPULATION IS the largest this island has known in the last hundred years. They are taller, healthier and better educated than their elders. Why then should they be affected by problems? The breakdowns we witness are specific to adolescence, a direct result of being a teenager in Ireland now: some of them from internal pressures, some from the environment of this country in the 1990s. In the early teens, one is facing new tasks and sometimes feels unable for them, or impatient at having to work through them.

So one finds children who do not want to grow up, who flee from the tasks and try to remain dependent on their parents, passive, seeking to have their lives lived for them. Equally, one sees youngsters who cannot tolerate the uncertainties of working for exams, developing one's own style, learning the trade of man. They want to jump into a fully-fledged adulthood without the pain of learning and experimenting. If some group (like the Provisional IRA, or the UFF, or a fundamentalist cult) offered them a package of *how to be an adult*, where one asks no questions and conforms to a totalitarian model, they may jump at it, with all the sacrifices it demands, because it seems less painful than the ambiguities of growing and learning.

THIS IS NOT A psychiatric paper, but rather a look at what parents experience as adolescent madness. Differential diagnosis, sifting out the evidence for psychotic illness, is a skilled and essential service. Adolescence is a high-risk period for the onset of schizophrenia, which will afflict perhaps one in a hundred teenagers, more probably where the sickness has already occurred in the family. If your Brendan is feeling that others have more influence on his behaviour than he has himself, if he cannot distinguish other people's reactions from the creations of his own mind, if he is regressing to childish behaviour and if his reactions to events are wildly inappropriate, then you might look for medical advice.

Long before that is in question, families can watch a young person develop oddities of behaviour that gradually alienate him from the family and make ordinary work and relationships extremely problematic. The writers of fiction

139

have served us well here: few psychologists have achieved such delicate and perceptive pictures of teenagers as does Pamela Frankau in *A Wreath for the Enemy* or Joanna Trollope with figures like Joss in *The Men and the Girls.* The quirkiness of the individual evades all the patterns in the psychological or medical textbooks. Every adolescent has his own temperament, position in the family, inherited vulnerabilities (such as liability to addiction or other neurosis). So his reaction to the tasks listed below will be tempered by his own style. We are all unique and unrepeatable, and no formulas do justice to us. Yet there are some clear tasks to face.

THE CENTRAL TASK LIES in the name: *adolescence* means to begin to become an adult. The Freudian tradition sees this as repeating the struggle of the toddler to stand on his own feet and say *no* to mother: to become a separate individual. It is felt inherently as an aggressive act, as though growing to maturity can only be accomplished at the expense of one's parents, even over their dead bodies. Puberty is a time of bereavement. Anna Freud called it the slow and painful ending of one's first love affair, boy with mother, girl with father. The little boat is pushing away from the pier that sheltered it. The more closely bound it has been to the pier, the more painful the process of pushing away.

The young body that pushes away from mother and father is itself changing, feeling an upsurge of instincts associated with sexual awakening. The psychic balance that has been achieved by the end of childhood is upset. He starts to direct his affections outside the family. With all its excitement, this period can feel, to both parents and child, like a bereavement, the end of something beautiful and precious. At a time when one's body is at its healthiest and most sensitive, there is a feeling of emotional flatness, loneliness and depression, resulting from the separation from parents.

One typical reaction to this flatness is to do things just for kicks, to show a hunger for intense emotional states, such as at parties, rock concerts, football matches, whether as player or spectator. After a separation you feel not just empty but unreal, and one of the hungers of the middle teens can be to recover that sense of being alive which for most of one's young life was found in the affection of parents and family. The company of one's friends stands in place of the family, gives you a place to belong and feel real.

Here is a more concrete summary of what growing up entails:

a) to come to terms with a new body, managing one's diet, sleep and appearance and learning how to care for one's own health, a job hitherto managed by mother;

b) to stretch an intelligence that is reaching the height of its powers;

c) to live with a turmoil of moods and emotions;

d) to learn how to cope with one's peer-group;

e) to get on with the opposite sex;

f) to accept one's own burgeoning sexuality so that, from being confusing or self-indulgent, it may become a mode of love;

g) to achieve independence of parents and have a style and identity of one's own;

h) to find a place in society by going to school, passing exams and seeking a job;

i) finally and slowly, to move towards a sense of what life is about: this includes accepting the reality of suffering and cruelty in the world, learning how guilt can be assuaged by work and dependability in a job; taking on the evil in the world without losing hope.

This is too neat. None of us achieves it all. The list glides over a number of ambiguities. *Accepting one's own sexuality* is not a black and white affair, straight or gay, but a unique, idiosyncratic cocktail which takes a lot of getting used to. *Finding a place in society* can be an empty phrase where the number of young people outnumbers, by tens or hundreds of thousands, the number of available jobs. *Taking on the evil in the world* is a grimmer task where that evil is thrust at young eyes every day in a meaningless, valueless way by films, videos and news reports. It is grimmer also for young people who have lost touch with the Christ who combated evil and sickness, yet could face suffering with love. The Christian sense of a meaning in suffering is often obscured in the parodies of religion that young people encounter.

PETER WAS A BRIGHT 16-year-old, holding his place comfortably in the top stream of a Fourth Year class in a good school. Then, over the course of one term, he stopped working and became stroppy within the family. He persuaded himself that he would achieve fame as a guitarist in a pop group or as the manager who would haul a group up to the eminence of U2. His cleverness was used to bolster his manic grandiosity. *You don't need silly Leaving Certificates in the pop world.* The fact that he had played the guitar for less than two years did not bother him. *I can always fall back on computers – I can manage eight different computer languages.*

His mother and father looked on as he undermined his life-chances by idling. They were tempted to treat him like an infant, for he talked like one, expecting the world to conform to his illusions, sniffing out careers, like the entertainment world or photography, where a Leaving Certificate would be less necessary and his genius would be rewarded. While he had a baby's self-centered thirst for instant gratification, he had the brain of a bright adolescent and could not be talked down to.

Nor would it help to take his illusions more seriously than they deserved. His mother gave up her job in order to stay in touch with him, and contrived, with many stumblings, to transform Peter's narcissism into more mature ambitions, ideals and the competent exercise of skills. His strivings gradually lost their infantile, imperious and sadistic quality, as he discovered it was safe to face the world as it is. But there were times when he seemed downright mad, and his parents were asking friends for the names of good psychiatrists.

Breakdown can happen where the young person, in face of the tasks of growing up, retreats like Peter to infantile attitudes, which are sustained with the bright intelligence of a young adult. The prospect of leaving the security of childhood may result in regressive symptoms like sulking, temper tantrums, obsessional activities, or a struggle to regain infantile gratifications: refusing to go to school or work, and expecting the world to conform to their desires.

THE OTHER FORMS THAT breakdown can take may be seen as depression in the face of the tasks of growing, or depressive equivalents, maladaptive ways of keeping despair at bay.[2] There are signs that suggest a more serious upset. An adolescent who is clinically depressed will usually show some, though not all, of them:

1) There is a mood of *hopeless sadness*, not warranted by what he has actually experienced. It is just there, and he does not try to justify it. He feels tired, lethargic, with no heart to tackle anything.

2) He has *lost the capacity for enjoyment*. The savour has vanished even from activities that normally give him pleasure.

3) He *feels worthless*, unimportant, and deserving of all the misery that afflicts him. He dismisses his real achievements, expects to fail and to lose his friends, and sees no reason why people should like or respect him.

4) A sense of *guilt* may complicate this: guilt for upsetting his family, for doing badly at school, or a vague, unspecified guilt for some larger crime that seems to cloud his conscience.

5) *Anxiety* may show itself in restlessness, inability to sit still or settle down to anything.

6) There may be *disturbances of sleep* (slow to drop off, early to wake), of appetite and normal bodily well-being, in the shape of aches, constipation or menstrual disturbances in girls.

7) He may seem preoccupied with thoughts of *death* or *injury*, and raise the fear of suicide by remarks, threats or carelessness about his life. These have to be taken seriously.

---

2 Parry-Jones, W., *Child and Adolescent Psychiatry*, Chapter 36, Blackwell, Oxford, 1985.

A list like this is alarming, but difficult to use. It takes the informed and practised eye of a doctor to diagnose clinical depression with any assurance. The aim of diagnosis is to lead towards appropriate treatment, such as is mercifully more available and effective today than thirty years ago.

THE TEENAGER, DAUNTED BY the task of growing up, may show behaviour or reactions that can be seen as depressive equivalents. One example is *delinquent behaviour*, such as stealing, vandalising, mindless violence, when it appears in a family or sub-culture which is generally law-abiding. Most of the crime in our cities is now associated in some way with drugs, including alcohol, the drug most popular with teenagers. But if you find a young person who is cold sober acting the delinquent, it can be a form of adolescent breakdown. A police record is a crippling burden for a young person to carry, limiting movement in the future, a skeleton permanently in his cupboard. Parents always want to save their children from the law and hate the thought of a squad car at their door. But we have generally good gardaí and some excellent Junior Liaison Officers, who treat young offenders with compassion, insight and appropriate toughness. Teenagers who have gone over the edge of the law are generally better served by facing the consequences of their actions, than by being protected from the law.

Another depressive equivalent is *running away from home*. A letter left on his bed by a runaway fifteen year-old boy puts it clearly:

> *Dear Mom, I will be gone just for a few days. Don't worry, I have somewhere to stay on my own. Everyone is annoying me lately and I am all confused. People say these years are the best ones. Not for me their not. You only live once and you experience things once. Your a teenager once and now's the time for doing stupid things like this. Don't go to any of my friend's house causing trouble with them. Just think that I'm having a break on my own. I shall ring you twice a day and tonight. See you soon. Love ...*

He did see her soon: he was back home before nightfall. He needed the gesture and the note to articulate his cry for help, and it worked.

Equally frightening is the *taking of wild risks*. Young people have to take control of their own bodies, and this is often done in defiance of mother, implying *I no longer need you to keep me fed and warm and safe. It is my body and I can do what I like with it*. There are times when this defiance becomes self-destructive.

Richard was an enormous 15-year-old who borrowed a Kawasaki 550, drove it helmetless, crashed while cornering at 85 mph, left the bike a wreck in the ditch and walked away unscathed, saying nothing to parents or friends. He felt himself an adult, bigger and stronger than his father or most of his teachers. Every day at school seemed a protracted insult, forcing him into the role of a child when he could hardly fit in a desk, with a daily diet of tasks which fed his sense of failure. This boy's anger and frustration led him from one enormity to another. In class he was miserable, but in a machine workshop he was intelligent, reliable and patient; that was the saving of him. It was the one area where he found some hope for himself, some recognition of his ability.

There are commoner depressive equivalents which are met daily in schools: *aggression without a proportionate cause, restlessness, poor concentration*. In the USA, where personal problems are easily medicalised, they may resort too quickly to interventions by medication or behaviour therapy, which put a label on the youngster (*attention deficit disorder, hyperactivity, conduct disorder...*). These labels have a specific meaning and function, but they are over-used. Parents and teachers are accustomed to the daily grind of setting limits to aggressive, restless or easily distracted teenagers. In general, more can be accomplished by the patience of the important adults in the boy's life than by professional intervention. If youth is a sickness, it's soon cured.

However, there are depressive equivalents which leave such a legacy of damage in a young person's life that they need professional help. Examples are the *disorders of eating*, and the *abuse of drugs* (especially the commonest drugs, alcohol and nicotine). They are dealt with elsewhere in this book. The abuse of alcohol is a particular menace for Irish teenagers. By the late teens, two-thirds of them have tried alcohol, and that is roughly the proportion who go on drinking (the drink companies spend their fiercest energies trying unsuccessfully to make inroads on the 33% of Irish adults who never touch alcohol). The problem is not the drinkers but the abusers of drink. One-quarter of teenage drinkers have been drunk half a dozen times and are on the road to losing their freedom and control over alcohol. It is the least effective and most destructive way of coping with the tasks of growing.

Another problem is *sexual promiscuity*, which springs in the young, as in the middle-aged, from a depressed sense of oneself. There are young people who have no sense of their own identity and seek to discover their true selves in a premature intimacy with a lover: two bodies coming together before either knows either him/herself or the partner.

DOCTORS SPEND YEARS LEARNING to read the signs of psychiatric illness and to distinguish them from growing pains. All the same it is the parents who need to be able to know when to call for medical help. What are the signs?[3]

When the young person is distressed beyond the point where parent or teacher can help;
when his lifestyle is obviously distorted (a sporty boy has given up all leisure activities, a sociable girl has lost all her friends);
or when the adults themselves are in distress for some time.

That is about as close as one can come to a check-list of signs of serious impairment. Where impairment is less serious, it all depends on parents knowing their children and keeping their nerve. Moreover, help is available. Some therapists are now trained for working with adolescents, a difficult task,

---

3 Rutter, Michael and Hersov, Lionel (eds), *Child and Adolescent Psychiatry*, Chapter 21, Blackwell, Oxford, 1985.

but one that can yield dramatic improvements over a short time. The difficulty comes from the young person's natural reluctance to have solutions imposed by adults. The improvements come from the huge dynamic in all young people to make something of their lives. If that can be triggered and hopefully sustained, the adults can sit back, or rather continue to walk the tightrope that Dr D.W. Winnicott described:[4]

> As adults, anything we say or do is wrong. We give support and we are wrong. We withdraw support and that is wrong too. We dare not be 'understanding'. But in the course of time we find that this adolescent boy and this adolescent girl have come out of the doldrums phase and are now able to begin identifying with society, with parents, and with all sorts of wider groups, without feeling threatened by personal extinction.

Further Reading

Rutter, Michael and Hersov, Lionel (eds), *Child and Adolescent Psychiatry*, Blackwell, Oxford, 1985.

Open University (Various Authors), *Parents and Teenagers*, Harper and Row, London, 1982.

Laufer, Moses and Laufer, M. E., *Adolescence and Developmental Breakdown*, Yale University Press, New Haven, 1984.

Copley, B. and Forryan, B., *Therapeutic Work with Children and Young People*, International University Press, New York, 1965.

---

4 Winnicott, D.W., *The Family and Individual Development*, Chapter 10, p. 87, Tavistock, London, 1965.

POST-TRAUMATIC STRESS DISORDER

FRED LOWE

IT HAS ALWAYS BEEN expected that major traumatic events, such as disasters, wars, and violent assaults can cause, in some people, persistent psychological distress, and lead to problems in re-adjusting to life afterwards. However, it has also always been impossible to predict from the degree of trauma itself who is going to develop these psychological problems. In the past, those who suffered from post-traumatic effects such as fear, avoidance of situations, fits of crying and depression, were simply seen as weaker or more vulnerable. As the evidence accumulated, it became clear that other more complicated factors were at work. For example, individuals who were deemed to be brave, as well as those who were thought of as fearful, were both likely to succumb in a similar way to traumatic events. Moreover, while most people were likely to recover their former levels of functioning within weeks, some continued to experience distressing effects many months and years later. It is the persistence of these effects in some individuals which is the most interesting and often puzzling aspect of post-traumatic disturbance.

While we have always expected traumatic events to have serious psychological repercussions on people, these effects were not studied in any depth until recently. It was as late as 1980 that post-traumatic stress disorder (PTSD) was accepted as a separate subcategory of the anxiety disorders in the third edition of the *Diagnostic and Statistical Manual of Mental Disorders*, known as DMS-III. For the first time, an attempt was made to lay down criteria to describe the most common effects, and as a result it provided a basis for research to discover why some people were affected in such a predictable way.

The DSM-III suggested that diagnosis of post-traumatic stress disorder should only be made if a variety of effects were exhibited over a period of at least one month after the person had experienced an event outside the range of usual human experience. Briefly, these effects can be summarised as follows:

* First, the person should re-experience the traumatic event persistently, either as intrusive and distressing recollections, or as recurrent dreams, intrusive thoughts or as sudden flashbacks. At the time of the trauma being re-experienced, the person also experiences the same feelings as at the time of the event. Also, as soon as the person is confronted with similar situations, they feel the same kind of distress.
* Second, the person persistently avoids situations resembling the traumatic event. This can be either avoidance of thoughts and feelings about the trauma or actual situations resembling the traumatic event itself. The person can also appear cut off and unresponsive to the outside world.
* Third, the person develops feelings of increased arousal such as sleep disturbance, irritability, difficulty concentrating, being easily startled, and a recurrence of the emotions originally experienced when confronted by reminders of the trauma.

No one would question that these listed effects are commonly seen in victims of trauma. The real question is whether there is a necessary cause and effect between the traumatic event and the feelings experienced thereafter. We know, in many cases, this is not the case. As I have already said, it is impossible to predict in advance the effects of a traumatic event on any one individual. One survey in the USA found that 31% of crime victims were still experiencing effects four years after being attacked, but no expert can predict which individuals will have to endure such chronic consequences.

It should also be pointed out that the range of traumatic

149

events listed by the DSM-III is somewhat arbitrarily limited. Witnessing violence, being the victim of violence, being threatened, are all allowed to be traumatic, but there are many other distressing events which are not explicitly included. The stipulation is made that the 'stressor producing this event should be markedly distressing to almost everyone and is usually experienced with intense fear, terror and helplessness'. This formulation does not allow for the fact that a few people may experience severe post-traumatic distress after an episode that would not distress most people or involve fear and helplessness. The debate as to whether people who watched the Hillsborough disaster on television could claim for the effects of trauma well illustrates this point. The fact that they were not at risk personally may not have been as important as the fact that they believed they were watching the live broadcast of their loved ones being crushed to death in the crowd. One woman was referred to me with all the effects of post-traumatic stress disorder – disturbed sleep, nightmares, exaggerated startle reflex, tearfulness and high anxiety – but they had been brought on by watching a television programme called 'The Day After', which dramatically depicted the reality of a nuclear war. To admit that she had all the symptoms of post-traumatic stress disorder, yet to deny that she could be suffering from it because she had not directly experienced real trauma, is somehow unsatisfactory. We have to concede something more intriguing is going on.

An important clue to the underlying factors involved is the observation made in the DSM-III that some events frequently produce the disorder (e.g., torture) and others produce it only occasionally (e.g., natural disasters or car accidents). It also notes the disorder is apparently more severe and lasts longer if the stressful event is of human design. Furthermore, all the research shows that the effects of trauma are lessened by social support and early intervention by trained professionals. Exactly why human cruelty and human kindness produce such heightened effects is one of the most interesting features of the disorder.

THE PSYCHOLOGICAL CONSEQUENCES OF trauma caused by human behaviour are best illustrated by the specific trauma of rape, where the long-term effects are better understood. As long ago as 1974, Burgess and Holmstrom described what they called rape trauma syndrome.[1] They suggested a two-phase reaction. The acute phase involved a period of disorganisation, dominated by fear, though feelings of anger, revenge and self-blame were also common. While some women showed their feelings through crying, sobbing and being visibly scared and tense, an equal number masked their feelings beneath a calm and subdued exterior. The acute phase of disorganisation passed, usually after about three weeks, and the victims then moved to the phase of long-term reorganisation, which could involve remaking family and social contacts, and reconstructing a normal lifestyle. A large number of victims moved house, both to signify a fresh start and to ensure safety. Most victims, however, never regained trust in men. The unpredictability of human behaviour seemed to prevent a return to the previous sense of security.

A necessary part of our ability to function in everyday living is what has been termed an 'illusion of invulnerability'. This belief that nothing is going to happen to us stops us being preoccupied with risks and prevents us from being consumed with fear. When a rape or assault occurs, victims lose this belief that they are protected within society, and they become disorganised and dominated by fears. Early counselling, which affords protection, sympathy and helps the victim to reorganise her life, seems to lessen the recovery time for most victims and prevents chronic consequences.

A SECOND CORE BELIEF which helps us to feel secure is what has become known as the 'Just World' principle. This refers to the conviction in most of us that there is an appropriate determinism between what people do and what happens to them. We think we control what happens to us and

---

1 Burgess, A. W. and Holmstrom, L. L., 'Rape Trauma Syndrome', *American Journal of Psychiatry*, 131, 9, September 1974, pp. 981–986.

that people get what they deserve. Traumatic events shatter this belief in two ways. First, victims of disasters or crime are often 'innocent' and do not deserve what has happened to them, and second, the perpetrators often do not get appropriately punished. When the consequences add insult to injury, we call this 'secondary injury'.

This belief in a just world tends to lead to victim-blaming, because we want to preserve the notion that people only get what they deserve. Many victims begin to blame themselves for not avoiding the disaster. They assume they must have been responsible in some way. They not merely ask, 'Why me?' but go on to make judgements such as, 'I must have been a fool'. Very often, either the authorities or other people blame the victim. Police blame victims for not taking precautions against crime, and some judges have been known to blame rape victims. One British judge notoriously accused the victim of 'contributory negligence'. Another young Dublin woman, who had been raped after a disco, was similarly harshly treated when her parents showed her no sympathy but blamed her for going out in the first place. When they then prevented her from ever going out again, she felt she was being put in prison for the offence of being a rape victim.

When the self-blame is accompanied by some other negative self-evaluation, the effect can be overwhelming. This can be illustrated by the following case-study. An experienced worker, working in a job which involved some risk, was involved with a colleague in a serious accident. When confronted with death – for they were both seriously injured – his instinct was to save himself. He escaped, leaving the other man for dead. Subsequently, he had to reappraise himself. He always thought he was brave and would help others in an emergency, but he had not done so. He had, in his eyes, run like a coward, and he was torn with guilt that he put himself first. This is the typical 'self-injury' situation. Self-blame combined with self-condemnation totally undermined his ability to function in his job and as a person.

Secondary injury may occur at any stage of the trauma

152

victim's subsequent attempts to recover. Being interviewed by the police, appearing in court and confronting the assailant during the trial, can all cause further distress and reactivate the original trauma. Often, physical injury or subsequent financial loss can serve as reminders of the first traumatic injury.

In some cases, this 'secondary injury' can produce more serious and lasting effects than the primary event. For example, one woman was mugged in town. She was not physically hurt, as she was pushed to the ground and then had her handbag stolen. She had always expected that passers-by would intervene and offer appropriate help. Only one or two people, however, stopped to talk to her. One of these, a woman, simply remarked that she did not know what the world was coming to, and walked on. The victim felt the police did no more than record the crime and had no interest in finding the thief or her property. When she finally returned to her car, she found a parking ticket. What shattered her was not the theft so much as the indifference of people and the injustice of it all. The combination of callous crime and public indifference turned her hitherto safe world into a very perilous and menacing place, and it was this altered perception which produced most of the fear symptoms she subsequently experienced. One of the hardest things to come to terms with is that the victim did nothing wrong and did not deserve the harm he or she has suffered.

COMPENSATION NEUROSIS IS ANOTHER much misunderstood phenomenon. It is often assumed that victims of an accident, for example, fake injuries until they receive compensation. Some unfortunately do pretend in this way. True compensation neurosis is where the mind blocks recovery until the victim is compensated for the injury, and sometimes beyond, even though recovery is strongly desired. There are possibly two things going on here. First, the traumatic episode of the accident is not seen as complete until the awarding of compensation puts a full stop to the sequence of events. For this reason, the patient's mind perpetuates the injury until the episode is over. Second, a sense of injustice, of unfair victimisation, hinders the healing process at a psychological level. For this reason, inadequate compensation is experienced as another secondary injury and further hinders rehabilitation and readjustment. Research with post-trauma victims in general suggests that where the outcome is unsatisfactory, people do seem to have more persistent symptoms and develop more chronic effects.

The complexity of the effects of traumatic events can be illustrated by another interesting fact. The symptoms of post-traumatic stress can affect not only victims, but also the bereaved and those involved in helping at the scene of the disaster.

The King's Cross tube disaster occurred on 18 November, 1987. In the fire, thirty-one people died and many dozens were severely injured. Most of those involved in the rescue operation ignored their psychological distress and bravely battled on during and after the event. Five years later, two of the police officers who were central to the rescue operation left the force and became unemployed. One had run the Metropolitan Line control room and the other supervised the mortuary to which the horribly burned bodies were taken. They were both diagnosed as classic cases of post-traumatic stress disorder. Their solicitor listed the effects as including depression, anxiety, nightmares, flashbacks during waking hours, distress at reading media reports of disasters, short temper and irritability. Fourteen firemen involved in the rescue also made claims, and one received £147,000 for post-traumatic stress disorder.

Dr James Thompson, whose unit at the Middlesex Hospital specialises in treatment of trauma victims, said, 'There will always be some suspicion and hostility about psychological distress occasioned by events, but there is more of an understanding now then there was seven or eight years ago'.

This earlier insensitivity to psychological distress is well illustrated by the aftermath of the Falklands/Malvinas war. A fleet chief petty officer, who had not come under direct fire, but who had been carried from ship to ship by helicopter, suffered a breakdown on his return home. After twenty-two years in the navy, he was invalided out and the

DHSS accepted that his condition was the result of service in the Falklands/Malvinas. The South Atlantic Fund, set up for victims of the war, however, refused to compensate him, apparently because they felt the causal link of his condition to the war was not established.

Recently, in the British Parliament, a Private Member's Bill was introduced to clear the names of the hundreds of soldiers who had been shot for cowardice. The bill was defeated as John Major said it was inappropriate to revise judgements in the light of modern knowledge. This is, I would argue, insensitive. Minds as well as bodies are the casualties of war, and it is not necessary to be under fire to become a victim of the brutality of armed conflict. Many chose the firing squad as the hell of going back in the trenches was intolerable. Had they been sent home with physical injuries they would have been made heroes. Because it was their minds which suffered injury, they were shot as cowards. An enlightened view would see them all as casualties of a senseless war. Post-traumatic stress is simply a less visible war wound.

MY OWN WORK SUGGESTS that anger is a much more significant emotion in PTSD than has been considered to date. When the traumatic event leads to loss of trust, a loss of belief in humanity, a loss of belief in the justice system and a loss of belief in a safe world, the result is often not fear but extreme anger. This sense of injustice and accompanying anger often leads to rehearsal of the traumatic event and to a heightening of the arousal system as a result. Where there is good social support and where the society at large helps to re-establish the values of the individual, there does seem to be a lessening of both the anger and the PTSD. It would seem important that the victims of trauma should be helped not merely by anxiety reduction techniques, but by a concerted attempt to re-establish the victim's value system.

The anger, in short, is because the victim finds the world is not as he believed it was. One of our central beliefs is that people get what is coming to them. This belief is doubly shattered for victims of trauma. First, they find themselves

155

the victims of disaster or injury, even though they may have done nothing wrong. If the injury is due to a natural catastrophe, they seem more easily to accept it as an accident or 'act of God'. Such accidents are rare and unavoidable. No-one is to blame. If the injury is caused by human malice or negligence, however, this core value is destroyed. Early support and help can restore it, hence the value of concerted social support, but if people get away with the evil, anger and distress can be permanent. The anger of the relatives and survivors of the Hillsborough disaster, where nearly a hundred died but no one was deemed responsible, well illustrates this lingering effect.

THERE ARE, IN SUMMARY, three areas which have to be addressed in victims of post-traumatic stress disorder.

* First, there is the horror of the traumatic incident itself. Here, psychological debriefing seems to be essential. Talking about the experience helps the person come to terms with it.
* Second, there is a need to reduce the person's sense of vulnerability. The more social support a person has the earlier this can be achieved. The person can then move from a sense of being protected to increasing independence.
* Third, there is the need to reorganise and resume normal life. This also involves restoring core beliefs, such as a sense of justice in society.

With these points in mind, victims of trauma should remember the following:

1) It is important to express feelings and to share the experience by talking about it. The importance of expressing these thoughts allows the trauma to be accepted and allows the emotions to find expression. For this reason, many countries have set up disaster services, which include group meetings, to allow for this 'psychological debriefing'. Hostage victims, such as those returning

from the Lebanon, were all given lengthy debriefing to lessen later trauma.

2) Attempting to forget about the event by undertaking activity and distracting oneself from the memories tends to delay recovery. Victims of trauma should expect to have recurrent memories and distressing feelings.

3) The use of alcohol, nicotine or prescribed drugs should be avoided if victims attempt to suppress feelings. Many trauma victims are prone to addiction because of this mistaken attempt to forget.

4) Expect a period, often lasting about a month, during which there may be disturbed sleep, nightmares and other feelings. This is a normal reaction to terrible events and allowing for a period of distress may be part of the healing and accommodating process.

5) Expect to lose some confidence and expect work performance to deteriorate somewhat. It is unusual to be able to concentrate when distressed. By allowing for a period of reduced efficiency, the person is less likely to see himself as either a failure or as hopelessly harmed.

6) Do look to friends and professionals for support. Many countries now have victim support groups, and one of the valuable services they provide is to give the victim the healing message that people do care. Accepting that we are vulnerable and can be harmed is one of the most difficult things for a victim to do. Looking for, and getting, protection seems to help people come to terms with this fact.

Above all, the victim and society must come to recognise that the emotions following trauma are normal reactions to abnormal events. We do not need to overcome or ignore fear if we have been genuinely frightened. We need to accept the emotion and learn to cope again. One of the most common requests made by victims of trauma is to hope that their minds can be wiped clean. 'Can you make me forget?' they plead. The answer is that they will never forget, but sensitive help and support will help them to live with their mental wounds.

Further Reading

Hodgkinson, P. E. and Stewart, M., *Coping with Catastrophe*, Routledge, New York and London, 1991.

Scott, M. J. and Stradling, S. G., *Counselling for PTSD*, Sage Publications, London, 1992.

Cohen, R.E. and Ahearn, F. L., *Handbook for Mental Care of Disaster Victims*, John Hopkins University Press, Baltimore, 1980.

Raphael, B., *When Disaster Strikes: A Handbook for the Caring Professions*, Hutchinson, London, 1986.

BEREAVEMENT
When the Abnormal May be Normal

THÉRÈSE BRADY

The loss of a loved one is one of the most intensely painful experiences any human person can suffer, and not only is it painful to experience, but also painful to witness, if only because we're so impotent to help.
(Bowlby, 1980)

LOSS IS AN INTEGRAL part of life. All of us will die one day; all of us will suffer the loss of someone close. Yet the knowledge of the inevitability of death does nothing to protect us from its devastating impact. Loss affects us physically and emotionally and can have detrimental effects on our physical and mental health. It gives rise to a multiplicity of painful and often conflicting emotions. It may change the way we view ourselves and how others view us. It leads to major changes in many aspects of our lives; in our social status and in our relationships with family, friends and neighbours. It may also have financial implications. The suffering to which loss gives rise can be destructive or growth promoting. Research has consistently shown that the availability of social support is a key element in the outcome of bereavement. And yet bereaved people often find that support is not there when needed. Many report feeling isolated and shunned. Their loss has cut them off from friends and neighbours alike.

Why do we feel so uncomfortable when confronted with the bereaved? Is it because it raises fears of our own death, or that of those close to us? Or is it because of our own sense of inadequacy? We would like to relieve the suffering of our bereaved friends and relatives, but just do not know how to do so. Confronted with our own impotence, avoidance of the bereaved offers an easy way out. Thus, at a time of greatest need, the bereaved may find that even normal day to day support is withdrawn. An understanding of the impact of

159

loss, an acceptance that the loss of a loved one will result sooner or later in painful grieving, an ability to tolerate the grieving and to stay with the bereaved person without the reward of seeing the benefit of our support, are essential to the provision of the kind of support needed.

This chapter will briefly outline the common and universal responses to loss, while noting the highly individualised nature of each loss. It will consider normal and abnormal responses and will outline ways of helping bereaved people to cope in an adaptive way with their loss.

WHEN CONFRONTED WITH A major trauma such as a death or the diagnosis of a serious illness, the natural response is to seek protection from the reality of the trauma by avoiding or denying it. Numbness, a dissociation of oneself from the events surrounding the trauma, as if these were happening to someone else, serve as an anaesthetic against overwhelming pain. The bereaved may seem controlled, even less affected by the loss than others less directly concerned with it. These reactions are frequently misunderstood, leading to an underestimation of the distressful impact of the loss. Denial of the reality of the trauma may result in rejection of a diagnosis of a terminal illness. Disbelief may lead to an on-going expectation that the husband who has died will still return home from work, or the deceased child from school. A common experience is to wake up in the morning as if from a bad dream, only to realise that the nightmare is a reality.

As time goes on, the reality of the loss penetrates the protective defences. The knowledge of the irreversibility of the loss may lead to acute anxiety. Anxiety symptoms such as hyperventilation, tightness in the chest and stomach may cause the person to believe they are dying, thus increasing their anxiety to panic. A sense of confusion, disorganisation and an inability to make even the simplest decision may combine to make the bereaved fear for their sanity.

Waves or spasms of grief, which often come unannounced, can seem to tear the person asunder. Tears welling up inside may be suppressed, for we have all learned from the 'don't be such a cry-baby' admonitions in childhood, that crying is not acceptable. The bereaved person may find relief in letting those tears flow when alone and safe from being an embarrassment to others. Preoccupation with the deceased is common, with pining, yearning and searching for the loved one. The bereaved may wish to go back in time to tell the deceased how much they loved him or her; or to change something in the events leading up to the death which could result in their loved one being still alive. They may think they hear the deceased's voice, or footsteps on the path; they may even follow someone in a crowd believing it to be the deceased. These experiences may recur over months, even years. For the absence of the physical presence of someone does not result in loss of the experience of them.

Feelings of anger and rage are not unusual. The bereaved may want to strike out at people or objects. Their anger may be directed at the doctor who failed to prevent the death or to take them seriously; against an allegedly all-powerful and loving God who has allowed a young child to die. The anger may be against the person who has died, leaving the bereaved to cope alone with difficult life situations and unresolved issues in their relationship. The anger may be self-directed. Feelings of remorse and guilt are common; guilt about things the bereaved did or failed to do; about the times they were irritated with or disloyal to the deceased. Close human relationships always contain a degree of ambivalence, a mixture of positive and negative feelings. In the early phase of grieving particularly, the negative rather than the positive aspects of the bereaved person's behaviour and feelings may be recalled, thus nurturing their sense of guilt. They may compare themselves unfavourably with the deceased now idealised in death. Envy and jealousy of others, emotions alien to them, may cause particular discomfort.

Feelings of hopelessness and despair are among the most difficult emotions with which to cope. For the woman whose only child has been killed, or the man who gave up his job to look after his chronically ill wife, life no longer holds any purpose. Those who would wish to help are readily caught up in this sense of futility and are rendered impotent by it.

Loneliness is inevitable. Loneliness when one is alone

and the absence of the loved one is palpable. Loneliness when the presence of others heightens the sense of being bereft of husband, parent or child. There may be continual and unsuccessful attempts to make sense of the death with 'why me?' questions reflecting a deep sense of the injustice of fate.

Death raises fundamental questions about the purpose of life and about life after death. Answers to these questions frequently fail to satisfy, as they are questions with which each person must individually grapple. Even among committed Christians, there is often anxiety about whether there is a life after death and whether they will ever see their loved ones again.

With time, the intensity and frequency of the grief reactions lessen. While bereaved people may at one time resent the cliché 'time heals', later they acknowledge that the pain of grieving eases with time. Grief travels at its own pace and in its own fashion. Just as it seems that one is 'getting over it', a sudden and unexpected rush of grief triggered by a memory or special event elicits once again the longing or desolation. This can be disheartening, leading the bereaved to believe that they will never 'get over it', and indeed many never fully do so. They learn to live with their loss, adapting to a world changed by virtue of that loss. To take on new activities and new relationships is not to forget the old ones. The nature, circumstances and consequences of the loss, as well as the personality and previous experience of the bereaved person, all have implications for that process.

LOSS HAS REPERCUSSIONS FOR many aspects of the bereaved person's life. It can impact on his or her physical and mental health, increasing the risk of illness and even of death. It has implications for relationships and affects family functioning, roles and responsibilities. Roles filled by the deceased are taken over by other family members. Where a father dies, the mother may become the breadwinner; the eldest son may be expected to step into the shoes of father and/or husband; where the mother dies, the eldest daughter may be expected to care for father and younger children. These changes can cause additional strains within the family.

They may be resisted and the taking over of the roles of the deceased by others resented. There may be resentment, too, about the expectations that the individual should be strong (i.e., should not grieve) and should care for mother and younger children, a resentment often accompanied by guilt about the failure to meet these expectations.

Loss impacts on wider social relationships. The wife whose status has been largely defined by her husband may suffer a loss of identity and the loss of a legitimate role in society. Widows often feel social outcasts; widowers may be at a loss in a social gathering. Loss can have serious financial consequences resulting in loss of income and even of home. The widow may have to leave the security of her neighbourhood; the children their school and friends.

Loss has spiritual consequences. While for some, their faith is critical in helping them to cope; for others, a death calls into question that faith. The bereaved may feel betrayed or abandoned by a god in whom they had placed much faith, a sentiment clearly expressed by C. S. Lewis:[1]

> But go to Him when your need is desperate, when all other help is vain and what do you find? A door slammed in your face, and a sound of bolting and double bolting on the inside.

Yes, the consequences of loss permeate all aspects of the lives of the bereaved, giving rise to other difficulties while co-existing with ones already there.

GRIEF AFFECTS EVERYONE, BUT not in the same way. Different people cope in different ways, some doing so better than others. While sharing experiences in common with other bereaved, each loss is a unique experience for each individual. Bereaved people continue to be more like themselves before their loss than like other bereaved people. The nature, circumstances and consequences of the death, as well as the characteristics of the deceased and of the bereaved, all have a bearing on how loss is handled.

---

1 Lewis, C. S., *A Grief Observed*, Faber and Faber, London, 1961.

The manner and cause of death influence the reactions to it. An anticipated death allows time for preparation; for the dying person and their relatives to discuss issues relating to the past and to plan for the future; to give and receive love and forgiveness. In contrast, the lack of preparation, the abruptness of change, the violation of a predictable world, make the impact of a sudden death particularly severe. Sudden deaths are often violent deaths arising from accidents, homicide or suicide. The fact that the death may have been preventable can increase the blame and guilt. If the bereaved was not present at the time of the death, anxieties about the fears and suffering of the dying person may be acute. Inquests and other legal proceedings may exacerbate their distress and delay or prolong the grieving.

A death by suicide is one of the most difficult with which to cope, bringing in its train, remorse, guilt, stigma and, not infrequently, resentment towards the person who took his or her own life. The survivor may be obsessed with thoughts about his or her role in causing the death, or about what they should have done to prevent it. An AIDS-related death carries its own fears, stigma and isolation for the person who is dying and for his or her family. For example, a gay partner may be overwhelmed with desolation and may often be excluded from the events surrounding the death of his friend. He may suffer from self-blame as well as from fears for his own death.

While sudden deaths are more difficult to grieve than deaths for which there has been some warning, the potential impact of an anticipated death should not be underestimated. Caring for a loved one over a long and often unpredictable course may leave the bereaved person physically and emotionally exhausted and socially isolated. The sense of relief that it is all over may be accompanied by guilt for feeling relief.

The impact of the loss of a spouse and the increased health risks which follow on such a death have been well documented. Yet longitudinal research points to the resilience of the widowed, with most found to be coping well within two years of the death. The effect of the death of a child is particularly severe and long-lasting. The loss of an older adult is often lightly dismissed on the grounds that the deceased 'had a good innings'. While the impact of a death on siblings and friends is easily overlooked.

Age, gender, personality, relationship with the deceased, previous history and concurrent stressors all have implications for how the bereaved cope with their loss. While earlier research suggested that the impact of loss of a spouse was greater for younger than for older widowers, and for women than men, follow-up studies have shown that two or more years after the death, it is frequently the younger widows who are coping better than the older ones, and widows better than widowers. The mourning of bereaved children is all too frequently unrecognised. The apparent quick recovery of the young child is more likely to be a function of an inability to tolerate prolonged periods of upset than a true recovery. Signs of a child's distress may be seen in bed-wetting and soiling, in excessive clinging behaviour, in problems with eating and sleeping, in fall-off in school work, as well as in a variety of behaviour problems. These behaviours may lead to punishment and rejection, leaving the child feeling isolated, angry and/or guilty.

The personality of the bereaved is important. The person who has always been anxiety-prone and dependent may feel particularly helpless and frightened about facing life without the deceased, wanting to cling on to their relationship with him or her, making adaptation to life without them more difficult. Those who have suffered from depression in the past may have a heightened sense of abandonment and hopelessness. Previous experience of loss and of other traumas and the way with which they were coped will colour reactions to the present loss. Other concurrent stresses may exist, for one major trauma is no safeguard against another one. The widow may have a child with a mental handicap; the widower may have lost his job or be physically unwell. Bereaved people have to cope simultaneously with the distress of the loss of their loved one and with many other demands, those pre-existing as well as following on from the death. How do they cope with so many additional pressures at a time when their resources are likely to be at their lowest ebb? In what way can they be helped to do so?

LEARNING TO COPE WITH grief takes the bereaved along a slow, often torturous and seemingly relentless pathway. To help them on their journey through grief, they need support, understanding and tolerance. A support which is sensitive to their differing needs at different times, needs which may be emotional, physical, social, financial or spiritual; a support which provides a sense of safety and security. One which is available without being intrusive. An understanding which can tolerate the unpredictable nature of grieving; that grief rather than steadily declining from a peak of intensity at the time of the death, may not properly start until many months, even years, later; that at times nothing that you do or say will seem to help. A tolerance which will accept the feelings which the bereaved express as authentic and legitimate and which will not seek to block their expression by too ready reassurances or exhortations. The bereaved need to express their emotions when and how they experience them and in ways that are characteristic of them. To cry or not to cry; to express feelings of anger, hurt, guilt, blame, desolation or none of these; to obsessively ruminate about the deceased, to feel sorry for themselves. They need to do so free from guilt that they are not grieving properly or that their grief is a burden on others. They need time to grieve on their own, as well as with others.

BEREAVED PEOPLE OFTEN EXPRESS concern that they may not be grieving in the normal 'expected' way. This can be an added source of stress for them. There is no single 'right' way to grieve. Each individual has his or her own way of grieving; the majority do so in an adaptive way. Yet, for a small percentage, grief reactions may be abnormal. They may be inhibited, absent or delayed; chronic or unresolved.

Grief reactions usually appear within a few weeks of the death. However, the failure to do so should not necessarily be a cause for concern. There can be good reasons for inhibiting or delaying grief. For someone who has had multiple

166

losses or who, like the mother of young children, has immediate responsibilities with which to contend, the risk of allowing the floodgates of grief to open may be too great. While the postponement of grief may be appropriate under such circumstances, failure to recognise that the grieving has yet to take place may lead the bereaved, and others, to believe that they have coped well with death. They are subsequently at a loss to understand the grief reactions or the depression which may occur months or years later. Unresolved grief is often a significant and, at times, unrecognised feature in clinical depression.

While the absence of grief reactions may be a cause for concern, so too are excessive reactions such as severe anxiety or persistent panic attacks which seriously interfere with the day to day tasks of living. Overwhelming or irrational despair is indicative of clinical depression. Other reactions, less directly identifiable with bereavement, include somatic complaints, alcohol abuse and, among young people, a variety of behaviour problems including stealing, aggressive behaviour and consumption of drink and/or drugs.

Grief may be chronic or prolonged with continual crying and intense preoccupation with the deceased. Life becomes a permanent memorial to the deceased. By their refusal to be consoled, and the endless repetition of the saga of their loss, the chronic griever alienates those who would wish to help. They may be perceived as selfish and self-indulgent, and urged 'to pull themselves together'. Those whose relationship with the deceased was unsatisfactory may be reluctant to let go of the deceased; those who were heavily dependent on the deceased find the future too threatening to face without them. Caring for a loved one may have been all-encompassing and excluded other relationships and activities. Now they find themselves totally alone, bereft of alternatives.

Factors which can interfere with normal grieving and make the resolution of grief more difficult include the following: a sudden and/or traumatic death, a socially unaccepted death such as suicide, an unacknowledged loss such as a stillbirth, the absence of a body, for example, following a drowning, or the death of a child. A conflictual or overly dependent relationship with the deceased, multiple losses and/or other unresolved losses, a previous psychiatric history, poor physical health and poor coping strategies all increase the vulnerability of the bereaved. Finally, a significant factor in poor outcome is the absence of perceived social support.

WHILE REACTIONS TO LOSS may include symptoms of anxiety, depression and others which are indistinguishable from those warranting referral to a psychiatric service, bereavement is not an illness. It is a normal response to a major loss. While it heightens susceptibility to physical and psychological problems, given normal acceptance and support in the community, few bereaved people should need referral for professional help.

That kind of support is, however, often missing today. As more people live longer and fewer live in tightly knit communities, there is less experience of death than in the past. Death and its concomitants are not allowed into our everyday lives. Bereaved people are permitted, even expected, to demonstrate their grief for a short time after the death. Thereafter, it should be controlled and dignified and not intrude upon others.

Grief which cannot be expressed openly in the wider community may be too intense to handle within the family. The needs of different members may conflict and be misunderstood. There may be a single identified principal mourner, for example, the mother, for whom others are expected to care, while their own grieving is unacknowledged. The children or the husband may hide their grief lest they unleash torrents of grief which threaten their own control. In doing so, they can be seen to be cold and uncaring. While it is helpful and healthy for families to share their grief together, the intensity of each individual's grief and the potential impact of one person's grief on another, may make it unsafe to do so. As one seven year old replied when asked by her mother why she had shared concerns with the psychologist rather than with her: 'I was afraid of upsetting you and I knew she wouldn't be upset'. So it can be important to find someone

168

outside the family willing to accept the emotions and tolerate the endless and repetitive ruminations to which grief gives rise.

Grief will not fade away of its own accord. It needs active engagement by the bereaved and others at a number of levels. The reality of the loss must be acknowledged and accepted. Seeing the body, recalling the details of the death, and gathering information on the causes of the death can all help in establishing that reality. Grief may be denied or suppressed, but it cannot be resolved without experiencing the pain to which it gives rise. Understanding, identifying and giving expression to the emotions of grief are essential. The legitimacy of those emotions and the right of individuals to express them in ways that are characteristic of them should be accepted. The availability of a supportive environment is crucial. The bereaved must also take responsibility for their own care by seeking the kind of support they need, and by guiding the actions of those who would wish to help.

Adapting to life without the deceased calls for letting go of the relationship with him or her, acquiring new skills and investing in new relationships and activities. There are many techniques and rituals which can be of help. For example, collecting photographs and sharing memories about the deceased reassures the bereaved that their loved one will not be forgotten. This can free them to engage in new relationships. Guilt may be alleviated by writing a letter to the deceased seeking forgiveness. Anger may be dissipated by physical activity, or by being able to express the anger to those against whom it is directed. The acceptance of that anger, though not necessarily the expressed reasons for it, can be very beneficial.

Attention to physical and practical needs is important. The bereaved person who is not eating or sleeping properly or who feels unwell in other ways should consult his or her GP. Major decisions at the time of bereavement should be avoided where possible. The bereaved should learn to care for themselves, to take breaks from their grieving and to feel free to indulge themselves in occasional, even regular, treats. Where personal resources and supports do not meet their needs, or where particular difficulties arise, the bereaved may need to avail of other help. An alertness to the factors which may interfere with normal grief, outlined earlier, will be helpful at indicating the kind of help needed.

THE RECOGNITION OF THE difficulties experienced by the bereaved, and of the risk to which failure to meet those needs gives rise, has led to the development of a range of support and counselling services. There are self-help groups for widows, for parents who have lost a child and for others sharing a common loss; services provided by trained volunteers such as hospice and parish bereavement groups, and by professionally qualified bereavement counsellors. There are mental health professionals including clinical psychologists, psychiatrists and social workers who provide therapy for those with abnormal or complicated grief reactions.

A careful assessment of the needs of each individual and family, and of available resources, both internal and external, will help determine what is most suitable for each case. For the majority, the requisite support will come from within the family and community. Where this does not suffice, support groups or counselling services may be helpful. Such services take different forms. Some aim to provide social support, others counselling; some operate on a one-to-one basis, others on a group basis. As each individual's needs differ, so too will the service most suited to meet those needs. In general, referral to services is preferable some months after the death. Earlier involvement can interfere with the natural support system in the family and community. Too-early intervention may lead the griever to overestimate how well he/she is coping. When the reality of the loss begins to impinge later on, the bereaved individual may be unprepared for the intensity of his/her distress. For some, earlier involvement in a support service or referral for professional help may be desirable.

Referral for professional help is indicated when reactions are excessive, distorted or unduly prolonged and where these reactions seriously interfere with day to day living. Professional counselling and therapy take a variety of forms.

Therapists may seek to bring the bereaved person through their grief by encouraging the release of emotions, by confronting memories of the deceased and reviewing past relationships. They may help the individual to view themselves less negatively and to move away from feelings of guilt, helplessness and worthlessness. They may focus on coping strategies, on problem-solving and self-help techniques; on identifying and acknowledging personal strengths.

Grief is inescapable. It is the price we pay for love. Its resolution calls for the acceptance of the reality of what has been lost and experiencing the pain of that loss. The initial preoccupation with what has been lost must be replaced by investment in the now and in the future. In the words of Nietzsche: 'Your nobility shall not look backward but ahead'. Memories once painful to recall, become a source of happiness.

Suffering can be enriching or stifling. Loss can lead to constructive reassessment of values, to a discovery of new personal strengths and freedoms. It can impact negatively on self-confidence, relationships and lifestyle. Critical to outcome is social support. A support which is sensitive to the needs of each individual, which is tolerant and available, and which does not set unrealistic expectations for the time that it takes 'to get over the death', or for the way in which individuals deal with their loss; a support which is not frightened away by feelings of impotence when the bereaved fail to gratify the helper by being helped, but one which is able when 'our hands are empty to stay our ground and share the frightening darkness with them'.[2]

Further Reading

Lewis, C.S., *A Grief Observed*, Faber & Faber, London, 1961.
Parkes, C.M., *Bereavement. Studies of Grief in Adult Life* (Second Edition), Penguin Books, London, 1986.
Worden, J.W., *Grief Counselling and Grief Therapy. A Handbook for the Mental Health Practitioner* (Second Edition), Tavistock/Routledge, London, 1991.

2 Cassidy, S., *Sharing the Darkness*, Darton, Longman and Todd, London, 1988.

JOB LOSS

A Psycho-social Perspective

EUNICE MCCARTHY

THE SIGNIFICANCE OF PAID work is multifaceted. It is a route to social contacts, it gives a sense of purpose to life, it conveys status and identity and it gives structure to the day. For young people a paid job opens a key developmental door to an adult identity. The result of withdrawing a person's occupational status thus threatens both their status in the eyes of others and their own sense of identity. Job loss impacts both on the external and the hidden functions of work. The external functions of work include intrinsic rewards such as pay and work conditions, while the hidden functions of work include a time structure on the day, regular shared experiences and contacts with people outside the nuclear family, a definition of personal status and identity, opportunity to build up knowledge, skills and insight.

The hidden functions of work help us to understand why work is psychologically supportive even when conditions are poor and why job loss can be psychologically destructive for so many when these supports that are important for people are not provided by the alternative systems or substitute activities for employment.

The deeper meaning of paid work surfaces very sharply when people are faced with job loss. On the positive side, these meanings are reflected in the following reasons for working:

* Gives a feeling of being tied to a larger society.
* Having a purpose in life.
* To be associated with people.
* Enjoy the kind of work.
* To keep interested, learning.

* Gives feeling of self-respect.
* Keeps one healthy, good for you.

On the preventive side, reasons for working have included the following: that without work, one could:

* Feel lost.
* Feel useless.
* Feel bored.
* Not know what to do with time, can't be idle.
* To keep out of trouble.

These responses, both positive and preventive (negative), as to how people feel about 'work' clearly suggest that 'not working' requires considerable readjustment. It has been pointed out that the typical employed man does not have a repertoire of alternative ways of directing his energy and internal resources and does not at present have acceptable ways of gaining a sense of relationship in his society which are sufficiently important to take the place of paid work.

In what follows, the nature and consequences of job loss will be firstly considered from a psycho-social perspective. While research in this area has increased considerably in recent years, it has typically focused almost exclusively on male employees. One has to look long and hard at the material on unemployment to find any reference to the experience (as opposed to the mere numbers) of jobless women.

Traditional attitudes towards women in our society have been blamed for this neglect of research on unemployed women. To complement the focus on male job losers, I will draw on the experience of a sample of unemployed Irish women in the Dublin region who shared the pressure and tensions they encountered.

THE 'ECONOMIC FACE' OF unemployment, which is being outlined by economists and politicians in recent times, presents us with numerous statistics, analyses and predictions. When one hears the growing statistical picture, one is faced with one of the disturbing faces of unemployment, that is, disillusionment and a feeling that nothing can be done. However, we have to reach behind the economic data to the people, girls and boys, men, women and their families who are struggling to cope with life without jobs. It clearly emerges that unemployment is a common problem, it affects both the unemployed and the employed, but in different ways. It is everybody's problem.

The statistics about unemployment are becoming known and are being put together. However, the pool of experience of unemployment and knowledge about it from the point of view of the 'afflicted' group has not been incisively brought together and delivered to those who are in more powerful roles.

As well as the focus on unemployment patterns and trends, it is crucial today to tap the experiences of individuals who have become unemployed – individuals with their unique distinctive personalities, expectations, previous experiences and network of relationships (family, peer group, communities).

One approach is to ask the unemployed (registered and unregistered, hidden, discouraged) to tell their stories. It is only by telling them, by communicating them that we will even comprehend our and their common problems. During the 1980s, when the unemployment situation was clearly becoming entrenched, the resources needed to examine or diagnose the human side of unemployment were not forthcoming, nor were they targeted to yield constructive solutions to the dilemma in which we find ourselves today.

THE HISTORY OF PSYCHOLOGICAL research in the area of job loss began in 1933, with the publication of two classic texts: *Marienthal* by Jahoda, Lazarsfeld and Zeisel and Bakke's *The Unemployed Man*.[1] Since then the study of the psychological effects of unemployment has blossomed and varied with economic boom and depression, respectively.

---

1 Jahoda, M., Lazarsfeld, P. S. and Zeisel, H., *Marienthal: The Sociography of an Unemployed Community*, Tavistock, London, 1933.
Bakke, E. W., *The Unemployed Man*, Nisbet, London, 1933.

Thus, considerable research was undertaken during the Great Depression in the 1930s, and declined to virtually nil during the expansionary period of the 1960s. Once more in the late 1970s, and into the 1980s and 1990s, with unemployment figures soaring, research has turned to the social, psychological and human side of this problem. Describing the process of job loss and unemployment, Jahoda, writing about the depression of the 1930s, summarised the research evidence. He delineated the psychological effects as following a patterned course.

'The first phase is one of shock which is followed by an active search for a job, during which the individual is still optimistic and unresigned and still maintains an unbroken attitude.

'Second, when all efforts fail, the individual becomes pessimistic, anxious and suffers active distress – this is the most crucial state of all.

'Third, the individual becomes realistic and adapts himself/herself to this new state, but with a narrower scope. The person now is identified as having a broken attitude.'

These phases match more recent descriptions of phase-type reactions to job loss. For example, Hill's (1978) work also suggests three discernible phases, which were called:[2]

* Initial response,
* The intermediate phase,
* Settling down to unemployment.

Initial response: this can be traumatic, particularly if it occurs at the end of a long period of work. More often, the response is one of denial and a feeling that nothing much has happened. The individual looks upon himself/herself as having the same occupational identity as before and still describes himself/herself by it. The person regards himself/herself as temporarily out of work, thinks that he/she will soon find another job, and looks around with a certain optimism. So long

2 Hill, J. M., *The Social and Psychological Impact of Unemployment*, Tavistock, London, 1977.

as the feeling of optimism can last, he/she can even enjoy this initial experience of unemployment, looking upon it as a holiday. Some take a holiday, and those without family responsibilities may even delay claiming any benefit. They rely on savings to tide them over until the next job appears. This helps convince them that the situation is temporary.

The intermediate phase: the euphoria associated with the initial responses quickly wears off. Savings are exhausted; the holiday is over; jobs around the house are completed; and most important, the first few applications for work have failed. The person begins to accept the identity and standard of living of an unemployed person.

Leisure takes on a different quality when one is unemployed; it involves staying longer in bed, watching more television or just lazing about – but lacks the sense of resolution this brings when one has a meaningful job. Watching television in the evening and watching it during the day, when one has nothing to do, can be quite a different thing. As time goes by, the unemployed person develops a kind of inertia that is psychologically debilitating. He/she feels insufficiently understood and undervalued. The terms he/she uses to describe his/her situation are 'depression'; 'boredom'; 'laziness'.

The unemployed person feels increasingly that he/she is becoming not only occupationally but psychologically deskilled. He/she is less able to make the effort either to search for work or to get back to it if a job were to become available. The researchers noted in the early stages of the intermediate phase an awareness of the dangers and a recognition of the need to struggle against them. But the isolation imposed by unemployment makes this difficult and the individual becomes obsessed with a sense of futility.

A twenty year-old man made redundant said:

Happy for the first two months – it felt great having a rest from work, and suddenly it all comes on to you – after two months it gets boring – it gets on my nerves – that's the main problem – nothing to do – sometimes you feel terrible – you can't get on with your friends, and you are always in a mood.

Settling down to unemployment: after a time, changes begin to take place. The person begins to settle down to being unemployed. Anxiety struggles and hope all decline and the individual (and if married, family), adjusts to the new lifestyle. As they increasingly tolerate this situation, the depression associated with the second phase might lift. The unemployed person may continue to look for work, making regular visits to the Job Centre and scanning newspapers – but without any more hope that work is imminent and the longer it goes on the more careless one becomes with oneself and about oneself. 'I sometimes wish I was dead and gone', is a comment frequently made. Research during the 1980s has shown that while a minority of long-term unemployed can make a constructive adaptation to unemployment, the most common response was a 'resigned adaptation' (Warr, 1987).[3] There was a reduction in aspirations, autonomy and personal competence.

THE IMPACT OF JOB loss on those out of work and their families varies enormously: there is a significant difference between two weeks, two months and two years on the dole. Whether shock is followed by optimism or pessimism is likely to depend upon age, sex, health and level of material and psychological resources, as well as level of past pay and final settlement, if any.

Young people who have never accessed a full-time job, as well as those who have only participated in short-time employment, can experience both emotional and cognitive outcomes that include boredom, demoralisation, anger, lower self-esteem.

A UK study which compared joblessness among blue-collar and middle-class workers found no significant differences in the general psychological distress suffered by each group (Payne, *et al*, 1984).[4] Further, it was shown that, typi-

---

3 Warr, P. B., *Work, Unemployment and Mental Health*, Oxford University Press, Oxford, 1987.
4 Payne, R. L., Warr, P. B. and Hartley, J., 'Social Class and Psychological Ill-Health During Unemployment', *Sociology of Health and Ill-*

cally, there are no community values of unemployment that actively support the middle-class. To fail to find a home for skills and expertise that seem on the face of it 'professional' does not galvanise support. Shame and humiliation were common reactions, regardless of the reasons for the job loss (Fineman, 1987).[5] Those accustomed to managing their own destiny found their lives gradually slipping out of control – they discovered that they were unable to put things right for themselves. Support was, at best, fleeting, and the pressure on a marriage could be intense. Thus job loss in mid-career became a private, introverted affair often mirroring the insularity of the middle-class estates where people lived. Those who survived best would ritualise an imitation of 'real work' by adapting familiar routines of dressing, eating, commuting, contracting to the job of finding work.

WOMEN CONSTITUTE A PARTICULARLY vulnerable group. Research conducted in the USA has shown that 44% of the households managed by women who become unemployed dropped below the poverty line. Research with unemployed women in a large Dublin estate (Ryan, 1988) examined the core support networks of unemployed women and men and found that both groups placed great emphasis on receiving advice and help from their families, especially the marital partner.[6] Thus, the family constituted the key anchor in the provision of social support. Unemployed people, compared with employed people, drew on their social networks of friends to help them out materially. Unemployed women valued participation in a community-provided personal development course. This experience enabled them to reflect on their own situation and provided an outlet for building new

ness, 6 (2), pp. 152–174, 1984.

5 Fineman, S., *Unemployment: Personal and Social Consequences*, Tavistock, London, 1987.

6 Ryan, J., Social Support and Mental Health among Unemployed Women in an Irish Community. Unpublished thesis, MA, Social and Organisational Psychology, Department of Psychology, University College, Dublin, 1988.

friendships, which in turn acted as a buffer against loneliness. Given that women are not a homogeneous group, more research is needed to understand the unique way in which women are affected by unemployment across different job–class situations.

The overall picture emerging in recent years suggests that job loss leads to increased tension in families. It has been shown that unemployment not only affects family functioning in the broad sense but also leads to deterioration in the health of the spouses and children of the unemployed. Wives appear to become targets of the frustration and worries of the husband. The marital relationship can be damaged as well as the general emotional atmosphere in the home. It has been argued that parental unemployment represents a major source of stress for children and that uncertainty is a component part of that stress. In areas of lower unemployment there is a certain stigma attached to coming from an 'unemployed' home. Children are caught in the web of heightened tensions, fighting, short-tempers, alcoholism and pressure to find a job.

EDUCATION IS A MAJOR help in reducing the stigma attached to job loss and is also likely to increase one's chances of obtaining a job (by either impressing a potential employer or creating one's own employment). In Ireland, a Vocational Training and Opportunities Scheme (VTOS) was put in place to facilitate unemployed persons to re-enter the education system. Recent research by Ormonde (1993), invited people who experienced unemployment prior to joining the VTOS scheme to share how they experienced job loss.[7] The most dominant response was boredom, followed by a lack of money, lack of structure, no self-confidence, low self-worth, a feeling of being miserable, and feelings of bitterness. These feelings and experiences mirror very clearly the findings of research in other countries. On the positive side, the VTOS

---

7 Ormonde, A., A Study of the Perceptions of the Unemployed of Unemployment. Unpublished Masters in Career Guidance thesis, Department of Psychology, University College, Dublin, 1993.

course members observed that job loss provided them with 'more time to think' and 'more time to do things around the house'. In all, however, it became clear that job loss heralded a total change of lifestyle and a total change of friends. It further clearly emerged that job loss was perceived to cause great psychological stress on the family. This distress included constant arguments among family members and lowered marital happiness. There was a feeling further expressed that the community did not offer any significant support, given that many people were already unemployed in their areas. The support (if any) received from state agencies was perceived as inadequate. In particular, it was felt that the state agencies did not understand what job loss was all about. Those who experienced job loss further viewed possible access to the world of work as hopeless – as typified by employers' responses, 'don't call us: we'll call you'. The overall feeling was one of being trapped in a dead-end situation, without community, employer/state understanding or support.

The second chance education course (VTOS), was clearly viewed by the majority as a new avenue, a road to building their self-confidence, their courage and providing the skills which would enable them to obtain a job into the future. The educational experience had already enriched their lives and returning to education was viewed as a key step in obtaining a better job. A major outcome of attendance on the VTOS was an upsurge in psychological confidence and self-esteem. Group solidarity was provided by other students and staff. It also emerged that educational guidance and counselling need to be recognised as an integral part of adult education and second chance education needs to be provided for the unemployed. Further, as highlighted by Ormonde (1993), there is a need to establish outreach centres for the unemployed: these centres in turn to be well resourced and user-friendly.

THE RELATIONSHIPS BETWEEN HOW unemployed individuals perceive their psychological health and how they spend their time are important aspects of their ability to cope with the stress generated by job loss.

* One important coping strategy is how unemployed people think about their situation, how they see themselves and their internal psychic resources. Positive views about the future, about oneself and others, can act as a key buffer to stress.
* Maintaining social links that involve active interaction with others also nurtures a healthy self-concept. It is constructive interdependence that is considered healthy, rather than extreme independence or extreme dependence.
* Planning daily activities both inside the home and outside, and achieving these goals and experiencing new activities, reinforce one's sense of competence and control.

JOB LOSS SEVERS ONE'S attachment to work. This brings with it a loss of the rewards and benefits of employment. One loses the social and organisational structure of the workplace, including the loss of workmates and friends. Self-identity is lost and the meaning to life is affected. Job loss sets in train a process of disengagement among the unemployed. The humiliation of being without work, the feeling that the 'helping' organisations are not helping, the impact of reduced finance on recreation and on socialisation add to the tendency to withdraw. Job loss introduces a new disorder into people's lives; feelings of security are disrupted and life becomes destabilised. Community, family and educational systems are poorly equipped and there are few resources to facilitate the unemployed to re-evaluate and restructure their lives. The patterns emerging from the research mapped out in this chapter demonstrate that the costs of job loss are not only economic but are also psychological and physical. Preventive approaches in the future require deeper consideration of transitional concerns:

* First, the transition to becoming unemployed must be eased;
* Second, steps towards new forms of learning, educa-

tion, development, need to be put in place;
* Third, new forms of alternative work need to be created and sensitively resourced.

Further Reading

Fineman, S. (ed), *Unemployment Research and Social Consequences*, Tavistock Publications, London, 1987.

Ormonde, A., 'A Study of the Perceptions of the Unemployed of Unemployment'. Unpublished Masters in Career Guidance thesis, Department of Psychology, University College, Dublin, 1993.

McCarthy, E. and Keegan, O., *Dublin's Adolescents: Changing Contexts and Needs*, Mater Dei Counselling Centre, Dublin, 1992.

McCarthy E., 'Stress and Unemployment', Paper read at Annual Conference, Irish Federation of Women, Limerick, September, 1992.

Sheeran, P. and McCarthy, E., Social Structure, Self-conception and Well-being: An examination of four models with unemployed people. *Journal of Social Behaviour*, Vol.22, 1992.

Ryan, J., Social Support and Mental Health among Unemployed Women in an Irish community. Unpublished thesis, MA, Social and Organisational Psychology, Department of Psychology, University College, Dublin, 1988.

Warr, D.B., *Work, Unemployment and Mental Health*, Oxford University Press, Oxford, 1987.

MANAGING STRESS POSITIVELY

ÓRLA O'NEILL

THERE ARE NO STRESS-FREE zones in life. Everyone experiences stress. We express our stress in various ways. Some say, 'I feel at the end of my tether'. Others say, 'I'm near my breaking-point'. These words capture a person's sense of being unable to cope with the demands of life. Stress isn't necessarily a bad thing. For example, the demands we face when we set about redecorating a room may cause us stress, but that stress can be a spur to creativity. Indeed, we can thrive on stress so long as we are in control. My concern here is with stress that threatens to disable us in some way. The symptoms of stress can be distressing. They are particularly distressing when you feel that your ability to cope with life is being impaired or when you fear that your health is at risk, or when your vital sense of self-esteem is being undermined.

I start from the assumption that stress is something we can cope with. Coping with stress means taking more control over your own life. You are your own best resource. In order to get the best from your resources it is useful to become more informed about what stress is, how it can undermine confidence, self-esteem and health, and how you can cope with it when you feel it is a problem. So what exactly are we dealing with when we talk of stress?

Stress comes with any change or threat we face. The stress we feel may come hand-in-glove with a troubling event in life. The death of a loved one, losing a job, forced emigration, these are experiences which can cause us profound stress. But stress may also come with a happy event such as falling in love or having a new baby. Major changes in life may cause us stress. Stress can result also from the wear-and-tear we experience over time.

So what is stress? We experience stress when the demands made of us appear beyond our own perceived capacity to cope. Stress is not simply something out there in the world. So the stress we feel isn't just the fact that our boss is arbitrary and unreasonable, or that the subjects we are studying are difficult. How we respond in the particular situation is a part of the stressful reaction. We might feel unable to cope with the dictatorial boss because we have been unable to assert ourselves. I am suggesting that a reaction of stress is like a turning wheel with spokes going to and from the hub. We are at the rim and events are at the hub, and pressures go back and forth through the spokes as the wheel turns. There is a dynamic interplay between ourselves and the demands made on us which determines what is stressful and how we respond, and this can change over time. We vary subjectively, taken one by one, in how we cope with stress. What is stressful for you might not be so for me. Even so, it is beneficial to look at some areas of life where we can take positive steps to improve our ability to cope. We have the resources to manage the problems that distress us instead of being passive spectators of our own troubles, feeling disempowered because life has dis-eased us. Each of us wants (in the words of the poet, Richard Murphy) to live 'at the hub not the rim of time'.

OUR WHOLE BEING – MIND and body – responds to stressful situations. For ease of analysis we can identify three phases in our response.

Fight, fright or flight: at first we feel alarm. Many call this the 'fight, fright or flight' response. Your whole being prepares to meet the challenge or threat. Your brain puts you on alert. Your heart rate, blood pressure, perspiration, muscle tone, and metabolism increase. You breathe more quickly. Digestion slows. Surface blood vessels constrict. More glucose is released into the body. Endorphins (like morphine) are released which raise mood and lower your perception of pain. Your concentration intensifies and you feel pressure to make decisions. Do you run from the problem? Do you let yourself become paralysed? Do you face up to it? There is nothing harmful about all of this. A runner in the Dublin marathon will experience this before the race. Problems may arise, however, if you become trapped in this phase. For example, when you prepare to meet an attack, your adrenal glands release cortisone which helps your capacity to resist. However, too much cortisone over time can weaken your immune system which helps you fight infection, and can reduce your stomach's resistance to its own acid and cause ulcers.

Choosing: in the next phase, your body returns to its normal state. It recovers from the various strains felt at the alarm phase. Capacities to return to this phase vary from person to person. A profoundly fragile person who feels mauled by the ordinary demands of workaday life may not move to this phase and may need to draw on the support of others. During this phase you can make decisions about how to cope with the demands made upon you. If you are motivated to deal with the situation then you will decide what practical steps are needed to resolve things. Given that we are beings with a capacity to choose, we can make mistakes. But we can learn from our mistakes. It is important that we are reasonable about, and to, ourselves at this stage. If we allow our thinking to become fogged up in negative or unrealistic thoughts then we impair our capacity to make constructive choices about coping. At worst, we can make destructive decisions. For example, to decide to drink more alcohol in response to pressures of work is destructive. Later, I will focus on some areas of daily living we might consider when devising a plan to cope with stress.

Exhaustion: if you become trapped in the alarm phase you will probably end up in a state of exhaustion. At this point the mind and body are disabled from dealing with stresses. If you experience such exhaustion and cannot find the resources within yourself to cope then you should consider getting help. As you move towards exhaustion you will experience some of the signs of stress: impairment of thinking, memory and decision-making, tiredness, helplessness, irritability, crying, angry outbursts, depression, broken sleep, tense muscles, sweatiness, palpitations, strained voice, nausea, diarrhoea. You might smoke more or drink more. You might eat too much or too little. You might retire to bed or become too active and sleepless. You might become a workaholic or find it impossible to work. You might become unfriendly. You might drive erratically.

Constant stress: some people experience troubling stress all the time. Constant stress makes severe demands on the body and mind. The demands have been linked to ill-health. If you are in a constant state of alertness because of constant stress, your ability to learn new things may become impaired. If your blood pressure remains high, you are at increased risk of suffering a stroke. Constant tension in your muscles can produce headaches and pain in your back. Changes in blood pressure can put you at risk of heart failure or diabetes. Basically, constant stress can be a factor in putting you in jeopardy of ill-health. It can lower the quality of your life. It can impair your ability to cope. It can undermine your self-esteem.

IN MANAGING STRESS, WE are concerned to avoid chronic stress and its harmful effects. There are three main areas we might examine when deciding on the basic elements of our own personal plan for managing stress. These are: how we think, how we mind our health and how we live. We have the essentially human capacity to choose, to face up to the challenge of making a worthwhile life. We can reflect, imagine, plan, act, revise. We can take responsibility for our own lives while availing of resources, such as health care, as we require them. In this regard, our mind and body are part of a dynamic whole. We can decide to behave in ways that help us to cope with stress, to become more effective managers of stressful situations. Consciously adopted behaviours can shape our body's stress response and give us more control.

1. BEING REASONABLE WITH OURSELVES

We are sovereigns over our own minds, thoughts, attitudes and ways of thinking. That is the way it should be. To prescribe ways of thinking would be to attempt to exercise mind control. There are no quick-fix recipes for thinking ourselves into a state of well-being. However, it is helpful to be aware that certain ways of thinking can impair our capacity to live an independent and worthwhile life, and reinforce whatever destructive stress we are experiencing. Here, I will give some examples of ways of thinking which add to our sense of distress, but before I do so I will underline the importance of a sense of purpose in life.

Each of us has a fundamental interest in living a worthwhile life, and in having the resources that enable us to face up to that challenge. A worthwhile life is not just any old life, nor is it a life which has been imposed upon us from the outside. A worthwhile life is a life to which we are committed from the inside, mind and heart. We need a sense of what is important and a sense of values which give coherence to how we live and give point to what we do and the relationships we have. Ultimately, what values we commit ourselves to are a matter of conscience.

Now I referred earlier to the importance of our inner response to stressful situations. Our values are a decisive part of that response. Viktor Frankl was a Jewish psychiatrist who experienced the agony of a Nazi concentration camp during the Holocaust. He wrote that his sense of purpose and meaning in life helped him to endure. Brian Keenan's book, *An Evil Cradling*, gives us privileged access to how a man's sense of values and purpose empowered him to deal with and transcend the arbitrary and brutal deprivations he experienced as a hostage in Lebanon. The point is that our sense of values provides the lens through which we interpret and respond to the situations we face, from minor frustrations to profound tragedies and injustices. Facing up to the challenge of working out coherent values allows us to clarify our sense of direction and provides us with a resource for deciding how to deal with goals, expectations, relationships, challenges, conflicts, setbacks, tragedies, injustices and so forth.

Certain ways of thinking can impair our ability to integrate our values and develop a sense of direction in life.

Rigid beliefs: sometimes we fall into the trap of allowing ourselves to become puppets dangling at the end of strings pulled by rigid beliefs. We might, for example, have inherited the belief that we should be the perfect selfless lover, and then cast that belief as a rigid rule in our life and relationships. The rule might be, 'I must be a perfect lover who looks after my partner's every need'. Other such rules might be:

I must become totally self-sufficient.
I must never cry.
I must not complain.
I must never make mistakes.
I should not think of my own needs.

For many people, unyielding beliefs and rules litter their lives like dry bones in a desert. Failure to live up to these rules reinforces stress. Of course, 'shoulds' and 'musts' are part of ethical thinking. However, we are more likely to arrive at more humane principles and standards when we think things through, revising and modifying in response to the demands of real situations.

Negative conversation: we frequently talk silently to ourselves. We sometimes encourage ourselves to positively face up to challenge. We work out problems in our silent, internal conversations. We can, however, add to our stress if we allow those conversations to be scripted by a severe mental critic who undermines everything we attempt to do and damages our self-esteem. Suppose we would like to visit the theatre to see a play, but our inner critic's voice says, 'Don't. You're too stupid and going to the theatre would be getting above yourself'.

Or you would like to go disco dancing or ballroom dancing, but the inner voice says, 'Don't. You're too fat and clumsy and people will laugh at you.'

Or you want to participate in some community group, but the inner voice says, 'Don't. You're too inadequate and no one will respect you'. This is probably very different from how we would talk to our best friend, so why do we give ourselves such a tough time?

We let our vulnerability injure our self-esteem, and then losing self-esteem increases our vulnerability. This is nothing but a circle of self-destructiveness. We might even come to rely on it as a defence against facing challenges. We end up finding a false refuge in stress when we avoid the anxiety of facing challenges. We prefer the constancy of stress for the anxiety of change no matter how promising and exciting change might be. We teach ourselves helplessness and learn to become victims of stress. We might prefer doping to coping, and find relief in tranquillisers. It is important to resist this and instead to talk ourselves into more positive attitudes. We see athletes doing this before vital races. It can help.

2. KEEPING PHYSICALLY WELL

Healthy eating: a wholesome diet and good nutrition are vital for health and well-being. If our diet lacks certain essential foods or nutrients then we are more vulnerable to tiredness and stress than we would be if we ate wisely. There is no ideal diet, no sure-footed recipe for health. Our eating needs vary, depending on our age, sex, physical activity, body size, heredity. We select food also in light of personal taste or allergies or personal conditions such as pregnancy. It is, however, useful to be mindful of some basic points.

Variety: it is sensible to eat a variety of foods. For health, we require about 40 to 60 nutrients. These include vitamins and minerals, proteins, essential fatty acids from animal and vegetable fats, and energy from carbohydrates, proteins and fats. No one food gives us all we need. A useful idea is to select foods each day from each of the following groups:
- milk and milk products (2 servings)
- meat and alternatives (2 servings)
- bread and cereals (3–5 servings)
- vegetables and fruits (4–5 servings)

Steady body weight: it helps to keep a steady body weight relative to physical size. Being very overweight puts stress on the body and interferes with the ability to cope with the physical demands of life, and can make us more vulnerable to illness.

Regular small meals: eating small meals regularly is usually better than eating 2 or 3 large meals, especially when you are experiencing stress. Doing this will help you maintain a more constant blood sugar level and avoid the symptoms of low blood sugar (hypoglycaemia) such as dizziness, nausea, tremors, irritability and hunger pangs.

Eating is about relaxation and enjoyment. So try not to rush your meals, or work while you eat, save problems for discussion at some other time. By following the basics of nutrition you can eat your food confident that it will give you health as well as enjoyment. Here are some other recommendations to be aware of: cut down to a minimum the amount of refined foods, sugars and fats you eat; avoid excessive salt; drink plenty of fluids; a healthy, balanced diet should give an adequate supply of vitamins, but if you are eating a very high fibre diet, or eating over-cooked and processed foods you may need to consider a vitamin supplement.

Caffeine and nicotine are central nervous system stimulants and so have a marked effect on our stress reaction. We consume caffeine in coffee (1 cup of instant has 104 mg, strong drip coffee has 240 mg), in tea (1 cup has 48–72 mg) and also in colas and chocolate. Reducing coffee intake to about two cups per day is a better choice. There is only one healthy choice when it comes to nicotine, that is to stop smoking.

Recent research suggests that moderate drinking of alcohol is good for our health (men: up to 21 drinks per week, women: up to 15 drinks per week). But using alcohol to cope with stress is ill-advised as it can inhibit the ability of our nervous system to react constructively to stressors, can cause somatic symptoms and can disrupt social relationships and cause more stress and problems than it solves.

Tranquillisers and sleeping tablets can be very useful when used for short periods, a few weeks, or during critical circumstances, and when accompanied by measures to explore and deal with whatever upset or stress is encountered. Help for stress does not come in tablet form and it is generally a good idea to try and deal with the cause and not the symptoms of stress.

Physical exercise: being physically fit and physically well puts us in better shape to resist stress and illness. Aerobic exercise in particular can ease stress by allowing us to work off tensions. Aerobic exercise involves slow, repetitive, rhythmic contractions of the large muscles of the arms and legs, and includes such activities as swimming, walking briskly, jogging and bicycling. We use 'aerobic' metabolism to produce the energy we need for such vigorous exercise and this requires that we use up a lot of oxygen and forces our heart and lungs to work more efficiently. The health benefits of aerobic exercise include a decrease in blood pressure, improved circulation and muscle strength, and also a healthy sleep pattern and mood. The basic approach to increasing aerobic stamina is to exercise vigorously for 20 minutes, 2 to 3 times a week, with the heart pumping at 60% to 80% of its maximum capacity. Anyone just beginning an exercise programme should have a physical check-up first, and start slowly with some yoga stretches and walking for 15 minutes every day for a couple of weeks and gradually move on to more strenuous activity. You can make physical exercise more enjoyable by being part of a group – join a swimming group, go for a jog with a friend and so on.

Relaxation: relaxation techniques help reduce stress. Relaxation means more than just sitting down and turning off. It is a skill that needs to be learned and practised. Relaxation techniques help us reduce physical and mental arousal. In this way they combat and balance out the 'fight or flight' response. The practice of relaxing helps to block the habit of responding stressfully to situations. There are many classes available and also audio-tapes of relaxation exercises so you can practice at home. The choice of available and recommended techniques includes: Progressive Relaxation – which provides a way of identifying tension in the body and then developing deep muscle relaxation, which will take a couple of weeks to master. Autogenic Relaxation – this is a meditative process and uses self-hypnosis and suggestion to achieve relaxation. Learning this technique takes several months and it should be taught by a suitably qualified person. Meditation – these techniques involve focusing the mind on one thing at a time (this could be a word or 'mantra' or an object such as a flower, or a sensation such as breathing) in order to achieve relaxation. A quiet environment, a

191

comfortable position and a passive attitude are essential to meditate effectively. You can learn to meditate within a few minutes but, obviously, the more practised you are the deeper the level of relaxation you achieve.

Slow Deep Breathing is a quick and effective way to short circuit our stress response. It steadies and calms us so that we can interrupt the cycle of tension and decide what we need to do to cope with the situation. Whilst there are many different types of relaxation, it is not clear that any one is better than the other. So find a way that is comfortable for you, one that you have confidence in and practice it and try it out in stressful situations.

3. WAY OF LIFE

We should be concerned to examine the way we live. If our way of life involves constant stress then it is important that we consider how we might modify the demands made upon us. In attempting to make troubling stress more manageable we might take account of the following points.

Social support: we need other people if we are to manage stressful situations well. What support is available for us from family, friends, neighbours or colleagues, influences how we cope. With social support we can discuss problems, express feelings, get a different angle on things, get information and obtain feedback. People with good social support tend to cope better with stress. It is important, therefore, that we realise what support and resources are available to us when we need them.

Assertiveness: developing an ability to assert ourselves provides us with a resource to deal with stress and enhances our sense of self-esteem. The ability to say 'no', to look for information when we need it, to stand over our rights when we are being denied them, to express our feelings and needs, all help to keep lines of communication with others open, and create conditions where conflict and stress can be tackled sensibly.

When you have a capacity to assert yourself constructively you experience an authentic sense of control over events. You can state your position openly and clearly and effectively. Assertiveness does not entail riding roughshod over others. It is a vital skill which enables a genuine dialogue of equals to develop.

Controlling demands: although there are inevitably things in life which we cannot control, we can attempt to manage those things that are under our control. Stress turns on the burden of demands we feel we face. We can look honestly at these demands. We find sometimes that there are demands we have imposed upon ourselves without sufficient reason, and we can decide to end some of those demands. We can also refuse unreasonable demands that other people impose on us. Scheduling the demands can also help to keep control of the situation.

A balanced lifestyle: a balanced lifestyle means making time for all the things that we value in our lives. Making time for ourselves, our family, for our work, for relaxation and leisure, and so on. This balance and involvement in life can help protect us against the negative effects of stress.

THIS CHAPTER WILL BE worth the ink if it makes you more aware of the areas of life you can take more control over for the purpose of managing stress. Managing stress is about managing change. The underlying perspective of the chapter is that we can become agents of change for the better in our own lives, not just passive victims who depend on others to tell us how to lead our lives. It is for every person to decide how life is worth living. Making changes can seem overwhelming at first. However, personal change and growth are gradual processes made up of small steps. If you have recognised the need to deal with stress in your life, then that is the first important step. If we make the choice to take more responsibility in managing stress, then we liberate our capacity to shape and enjoy life, to meet its challenges and embrace its risks according to our own lights.

Further Reading

Patel, C., *The Complete Guide to Stress Management*, MacDonald Optima Publications, London, 1989.
Davis, M., Eshelman, E.R., McKay, M., *The Relaxation and Stress Reduction Workbook* (Third Edition), New Harbinger Publications, Oak-

land, California, 1988.
Charlesworth, E., Nathan, R. S., *Stress Management – A Comprehensive Guide to Your Well-Being*, Corgi, London, 1987.
Sharpe, R., *Assert Yourself*, Kogan Page Publications, London, 1989.

COPING WITH PRESSURE
Some Lessons from Sport Psychology

AIDAN MORAN

Under pressure, pushing down on me, pressing down on you, no man ask for; Under pressure that burns a building down, splits a family in two, puts people on streets ...
(Queen and David Bowie)

Pressure is the essence of the Ryder Cup. It calls for heart and guts. Guys have to expect that playing for their country
(Tom Watson)

Nothing in competitive golf prepares you for the sort of pressure involved
(Christy O'Connor)

Put 'em under pressure
(Jack Charlton)

IF YOU ARE THE kind of person who never has time to attend 'time-management' courses, or who is so impatient that you 'fast forward' your way through relaxation tapes, then you know a lot about pressure! If so, from bitter experience, you probably feel that there is very little you can do to avoid this unpleasant state of affairs. Perhaps you agree with the Queen song which suggests that we are always 'under pressure'.

But in this chapter, I shall explain why psychologists believe that pressure is neither inevitable nor insuperable in our lives. Furthermore, exploring insights from the world of sport, I shall argue that many of the psychological techniques which top athletes use to cope with competitive pressure can be applied successfully to everyday situations.

Although pressure is encountered in all walks of life, it is especially prevalent in competitive sport simply because the challenge of all competition is to determine a winner. Psychologically, the ability to *control* pressure is widely regarded as the key to winning. Two examples from Ireland's wonderful World Cup campaign in Italy will illustrate this point. On the one hand, Jack Charlton's management tactic of deliberately exerting pressure on opponents led to the unforced error by Steve McMahon, which allowed Kevin Sheedy to score Ireland's equaliser in the 1-1 draw with England in Sardinia. On the other hand, David O'Leary showed a remarkable ability to withstand pressure during Ireland's famous penalty 'shoot-out' against Romania in the World Cup in 1990. What went through his mind as he ran up to take that crucial kick? Like most athletes in a pressure situation, O'Leary concentrated only on what he had to do – not on what *might* happen if he failed. Therefore, he decided precisely where he was going to place the ball and he let his foot do the rest.

Perhaps the most remarkable aspect of O'Leary's performance was not the fact that he scored, but that he had volunteered to take the vital penalty kick in the first place. After all, he is a defender, had never taken a penalty in a competitive match in his career and had been on the pitch for less than 30 minutes (having been sent on as a substitute for Stephen Staunton) before the dramatic 'shoot out' occurred. But O'Leary's great self-confidence, developed over many years of experience in handling cup-tie pressures, quenched any doubts about his penalty-taking. It is this confidence, or feeling that one has coped successfully with similar situations in the past, which is the athlete's greatest ally when under pressure. Therefore, it is not surprising that athletes are being encouraged increasingly to train under simulated pressure situations in order to develop mental strength in competition. The logic of this approach is that 'practice under pressure makes perfect under pressure'. We shall return to 'simulation training' later. In passing, however, it is interesting to contrast O'Leary's composure under pressure with the anxiety of Gary Lineker, one of soccer's greatest strikers, who failed to equal Bobby Charlton's scoring record for England because he missed a penalty-kick in the 1-1 draw against Brazil at Wembley in 1992. Clearly, technical skill is not an accurate predictor of who will respond best to competitive pressure. It is this type of incongruity which makes sport such a fascinating field for psychologists.

IT IS WIDELY AGREED that the relentless pressure to win places a great deal of emotional strain on top athletes. For example, after Bernhard Langer had missed a short putt which would have earned a victory for Europe in the 1991 Ryder Cup match with the US, he sat alone in the team-trailer and cried. Fortunately, he was consoled later by fellow teammate, Seve Ballesteros, who suggested that 'no one could have made that putt: Jack Nicklaus in his prime couldn't have made it'. But this sympathy for performers who buckle under pressure is not readily apparent among sports fans. Thus, in explaining the remarkable rise in popularity of the Ryder Cup series, a commentator claimed that 'spectators are developing a form of blood-lust as they watch the climactic stage, waiting and hoping for a player to crack under the pressure'. This vicarious pleasure which fans obtain from watching athletes coping with pressure may help to account for the appeal of such volatile sports stars as John McEnroe.

So how do athletes avoid 'cracking' under pressure? As we shall see, most of the techniques which they use in order to remain calm and 'focused' during competition are derived from just a few psychological principles of pressure regulation. These principles, which athletes usually acquire through personal experience rather than through formal instruction, may be explained briefly as follows.

First, most athletes realise that it is our *interpretation* (or 'appraisal') of a situation rather than the objective event itself which influences how we think, feel and react when we are under pressure. To illustrate, consider the mounting pressure experienced by basketball players in the final seconds of important matches where a 'shooter's' throw may mean the difference between victory and defeat. Whereas most of us would recoil from such situations, notice the relish with which basketballer, Dennis Johnson (of the Phoenix Suns), tackles them: 'I'm probably the worst shooter of the five players on the court for the Suns. But when the game is coming down to the final seconds, I want the shot. It's not a point of accuracy; it's poise, confidence and *loving the pressure'*.

'Loving the pressure' is a rare quality which stems from an extraordinary level of self-confidence. Clearly, because Johnson is confident about the reliability of his shooting skills (i.e., he displays high 'self-efficacy'), he thrives on occasions when they are tested to the limit. But what is the source of such confidence? Psychologists believe that self-efficacy is determined not only by experiencing past successes in similar situations but also by developing accurate awareness of our own mental strengths and weaknesses, i.e., 'metacognitive' factors. If we know how good we are, then we should not be frightened of situations which challenge us. This insight suggests an important principle in combating pressure: if we can interpret a difficult situation as a challenge to our abilities, and if we are confident that we have the capacity to meet this challenge, then we need not experience pressure. It is this crucial role of *perception* in shaping our behaviour which convinces psychologists that pressure is *not* inevitable. By perceiving the world differently, we can experience a different reality. Of course, few of us can hope to emulate ice-cool performers like Dennis Johnson in responding to difficult circumstances. But we can all benefit from analysing the strategies which he and other successful athletes employ to counteract pressure in competitive situations.

The second 'pressure principle' used by athletes concerns the importance of maintaining *control* over their own behaviour in any pressure situation. To illustrate, imagine all of the time and energy which we waste every day by worrying about hypothetical events which we cannot influence. This rumination is understandable but debilitating because in dwelling on what we cannot control, we allow ourselves to be distracted from tackling the task at hand. Accordingly, athletes, under pressure, are encouraged to think only of what they must do at that moment, step by step. For example, if you are faced with a 5-feet putt to win a golf tournament, you should not worry about what *might* happen if you miss it but instead, you should focus on the slope of the green, the proposed line of the putt and the feeling of 'guiding' the ball into the hole. Accordingly, specific self-instructions and positive images should replace negative thoughts because, as Johnny Miller, the former US Open and British Open golf champion, remarked: 'If you hate or dread being in the position to choke, chances are you'll choke'. Put simply, by controlling your own *performance*, the results will take care of themselves. This focus on performance, rather than outcome, increases our resistance to pressure.

The third principle of pressure control concerns the importance of ensuring *proper preparation* for performance. Most athletes realise that systematic preparation is the key to optimal performance under adverse circumstances. Accordingly, in order to remain 'focused', they set specific short-term goals for their performance and tend to follow a consistent behavioural routine before executing key skills (especially those which can be performed without interference from opponents and at one's own pace: 'closed' skills). For example, notice how top golfers take the same number of practice swings before addressing the ball or how top rugby place-kickers follow a certain series of actions when stepping backward before kicking for goal. In each case, these athletes have been trained to focus their concentration on controlling their own behaviour rather than on 'fortune telling' the future. In sport psychology, therefore, the use of 'pre-performance routines' is widely encouraged. These routines, comprising deliberate sequences of images, thoughts and actions which athletes engage in prior to performance, help athletes to establish appropriate concentration levels for competition. Resembling the steps of a stairs, routines lead athletes to optimal 'heights' of performance. This use of pre-performance routines suggests another coping technique which has general applicability: you can alleviate pressure by *focusing your mind* on actions which break up the problem into stages. By controlling what you worry about, you are building an immunity to pressure.

But is there a danger that pre-performance routines could become stereotyped mannerisms which have mere superstitious significance? Hopefully not, because psychologists distinguish sharply between athletes who use a systematic routine to prepare for a 'pressure situation' and those who cling to a superstitious ritual out of fear or compulsion. To explain, athletes who have devised well-grounded, pre-performance routines as part of their psychological preparation for competition can usually modify them to suit different circumstances. But athletes whose rituals are essentially superstitious feel compelled to perform stereotyped behaviour in a rigid manner. For example, they feel that they *have* to wear a lucky shoe or a favourite item of clothing before a match simply because this behaviour brought them luck in the past. Clearly, this type of behaviour is irrational and can become self-defeating as the chain of compulsions increases.

THE OBJECTIVE OF THIS CHAPTER is to explore the main psychological techniques which help people (especially athletes) to cope effectively with pressure. These techniques are drawn both from cognitive behaviour modification and from cognitive sport psychology. Before explaining them, however, we must examine the nature and origins of pressure in everyday life.

According to the Oxford English Dictionary, the word 'pressure' has several meanings. Literally, it refers to 'the force exerted by one body on another by its weight'. But it also has several figurative meanings. For example, pressure may denote a form of social influence (e.g., 'She put pressure on me to change my mind') or a mental state 'of trouble or embarrassment; stress; strain'.

In general, pressure arouses bodily tension. And because tension is usually aversive, then one might expect that people would attempt to reduce pressure, or perhaps avoid it altogether. But this is not the case as some people seem to be attracted to pressure situations. For example, 'Type A' individuals (i.e., competitive, 'hard-driving' people who display a constant sense of urgency) regularly create pressure for themselves (e.g., by trying to perform more tasks within a given duration than is apparently possible). In addition,

200

'sensation seekers' enjoy participation in high-risks sports such as sky-diving and rock climbing because of the thrill of being tested to their physical limits. Perhaps it is true, as some psychologists claim, that most of what we do in our leisure time is directed to the attainment of high arousal.

The preceding examples highlight the complexity of people's attitudes to pressure. Indeed, the arousal which it evokes may be interpreted differently by different people. For example, top-class athletes realise that some pressure is necessary for them to achieve optimal performance in their sport. That is why they usually welcome the experience of being 'psyched up', 'pumped up' or 'juiced' before competitions. Conversely, athletes who suffer from 'performance anxiety' may interpret identical signs of physiological arousal as harbingers of disaster. Clearly, it is the way in which we label our arousal which determines whether we feel 'challenged' or 'overwhelmed'.

Psychologists have pinpointed this fear of being overwhelmed as the epitome of the pressure experience. Accordingly, they believe that it arises when an imbalance exists between the perceived demands of a situation and the perceived coping ability of an individual. But this imbalance arises from a subjective appraisal of the situation – an appraisal which could be altered through the use of cognitive 'self-regulation' strategies. We shall discuss these coping techniques later, but first, a brief note on terminology. Is pressure just another word for 'stress'?

Due to its widespread popular usage, the term 'stress' appears to have a clear and recognisable meaning. It seems to capture our everyday experience of helpless frustration in the face of pressure. But for many psychologists, 'stress' is a rather confusing concept. First, it seems that apparently opposite circumstances can elicit similar stress responses. For example, people find both under-work and over-work equally debilitating. In addition, 'stress' is a vague and somewhat ambiguous term. Notice how it can refer either to an objective *stimulus* (e.g., 'the Leaving Cert exams caused me great stress') or to a subjective *response* to some unknown situation ('everything gets to me – I'm constantly "stressed out" these days'). Finally, it seems to be over-inclusive. To illustrate, one psychologist defined it as 'any demand, either of a physical or psychological nature, encountered in the course of living'. This definition suggests that everything is stressful – not just potentially so! For these reasons, I prefer to use the more familiar word 'pressure' instead of the term 'stress'. Having analysed what pressure is, let us now consider briefly what causes it.

Most psychologists assume that pressure is determined by 'appraisal' – the way in which we perceive and interpret a given situation. This appraisal process is influenced by a number of factors: the amount of *previous experience* which the person has had in the situation in question; his/her *confidence in relevant abilities* (i.e., his/her 'self-efficacy'); the degree of *uncertainty* in the situation (i.e., its predictability); the perceived *importance* of the situation; and the perceived *control* which the person can exert over it. As we shall see, these factors give us important clues as to how we can control pressure.

Although these determinants of pressure can be distinguished conceptually, they overlap considerably in practice. For example, one's confidence in tackling a future challenge is related to one's previous experience of handling similar situations in the past. Research also suggests that the more uncertain a situation is, the greater the likelihood that pressure will arise. Therefore, the more this uncertainty is reduced through advance preparation and background knowledge, the less pressure will be encountered. An interesting trend in sport psychology is to arrange for performers to simulate pressure situations in practice so that they will be immune to them in competition. For example, the current Olympic champion rifle-shooter, Lee Eun-Chul, from Korea, revealed that 'we practice the finals every day ... we don't get nervous because we train a lot to get used to the situation'. Finally, the person's perception of control over challenging events is very important. The more that people feel in control of them, the less the stress experienced. Indeed, some researchers claim that control need not be *actually* available to the person for stress reduction to occur: *perception* of

202

control is what really matters.

By exploring how these variables interrelate, we can identify some useful coping strategies. For example, there is evidence that a programme of 'mental practice', or 'visualisation' (i.e. forming and experiencing vivid mental images of successful outcomes) not only increases athletes' self-efficacy but also improves their performance. This finding is probably attributable to the fact that systematic mental rehearsal gives practitioners a vital sense of control over future events.

SO FAR, WE HAVE examined some general principles which suggest how pressure arises. But in daily life, people vary greatly in their vulnerability to stress. Indeed, some people seem to be almost impervious to pressure. These resilient people are thought to possess a personality profile (labelled the 'hardy personality'), which is characterised by a strong sense of self-esteem, a feeling of being in control of things and a tendency to view pressure as a challenge rather than as a threat. Interestingly, it is precisely this personality profile which personifies the principles of pressure control discovered by many sports stars.

In general, 'coping' refers to any efforts which a person makes to master, reduce or otherwise tolerate pressure. Technically, it has been defined as the things people do to avoid being harmed by life stresses. The key word here is 'efforts' because psychologists do not assume that all coping is successful. Accordingly, we should not confuse coping *strategies* with coping *efficacy*.

Research evidence suggests that coping efforts fall into two main categories. Some people like to 'take the bull by the horns' and confront the pressure situation directly. This is known as 'problem-focused' coping and involves such activities as obtaining as much information as possible about the pressure to be faced or forming an action-plan to reduce it. Alternatively, in 'emotion-focused' coping, people think of changing *themselves* rather than the pressure situation. Therefore, they may immerse themselves in relaxation or fitness training. In general, whereas 'problem-focused' coping techniques are useful in dealing with 'controllable' sources of pressure, 'emotion-focused' strategies are advocated when the stressors we face are perceived as predictable but uncontrollable.

LET US NOW EXPLORE the main techniques which athletes use to cope with pressure. In general, these techniques are believed to work by helping people to retain control over their own mental states (e.g., concentration) and behaviour despite the presence of distractions. Accordingly, these techniques are commonly known as 'self-regulation' methods.

Athletes learn to cope with pressure by using at least four psychological processes: systematic preparation, constructive perception, 'focused' imagination and positive 'self-talk'.

Proper *preparation* for handling pressure in sport may be achieved by using the following techniques. First, athletes are encouraged to set specific, controllable goals for their performance before they compete. For example, a tennis player may set a target of 70% accuracy on his/her first serve. As in the opening example of David O'Leary's penalty, setting specific goals helps performers to concentrate on what they must *do* rather than on what they must avoid. Second, they are trained to adhere to consistent pre-match or pre-performance routines. For example, goalkeepers like Packie Bonner always take time, long before the kick-off, to practice a routine of shot-stopping 'drills' to ensure maximum alertness for important matches. This practice ensures that performers remain in control of their performance. Finally, the practice of systematically exposing athletes to simulated pressure situations (referred to earlier as 'simulation' or 'adversity' training) is being used increasingly to familiarise performers with competitive pressures. For example, tennis players can learn to handle the pressure of trailing in a close match by performing drills in which they must begin a 'tie-break' at 0–3 down.

Next, athletes are encouraged to *perceive* forthcoming events as opportunities to display their talents (the 'challenge' perception) rather than as potential sources of failure (the 'choking' perception). Third, vivid *mental rehearsal* (or 'visualisation' of how one should behave in the pressure situation) allows performers to familiarise themselves with the anticipated pressures and to 'automate' appropriate coping skills. It also serves to 'programme' the mind with images of success rather than overwhelming it with the fear of failure. Finally, athletes are trained to *talk themselves through* pressure situations by giving themselves specific instructions to follow before, during and after the anticipated difficulties. Let us now explain how each of these techniques can be applied to everyday life.

PROPER PREPARATION IS ONE of the most powerful ways of coping with pressure. As we saw earlier, obtaining information about the nature of the impending difficulty (a form of 'problem-focused' coping) helps people to reduce the uncertainty and stress which surrounds that which is unknown. Also, by developing a routine to follow in the stressful situation, people can learn to remain calm and 'focused' when the pressure is encountered. Finally, testing oneself under simulated pressure conditions (e.g., if preparing for an examination) not only familiarises oneself with the demands of the challenge to be faced but also increases one's confidence in one's coping skills.

Most people accept that the way in which we look at, or think about, situations makes a difference to how we react to them. Restructuring these situations in our minds may help us to respond to them more constructively. Otherwise, we may draw damaging conclusions from our experience. For example, we may over-generalise when we conclude that a failure experienced in one situation is bound to be repeated in different situations in the future. Similarly, we may tend to blow things out of proportion (or 'catastrophise' events) when telling ourselves that we will 'die' if we fail to cope successfully with a given problem.

In order to counteract these perceptual habits, psychologists recommend that we should use 'cognitive restructuring' techniques to look at pressure situations constructively. We can do this by asking ourselves certain questions before facing stressful circumstances. First, what are the *facts* surrounding the pressure which I face in this situation? What exactly is at stake? Remember that knowing what to expect from the task ahead not only reduces uncertainty surrounding it but also increases our sense of control. Second, what is the *specific task* which I face? What exactly am I being asked to do or achieve? This question is valuable because it clarifies our goals and forces us to look *outwards*, at our actions, rather than *inwards*, at our worries or doubts. Third, does this situation represent a threat, signalling potential danger, or could it be seen as a challenge which provides an opportunity to show my skills? Next, in considering my ability to handle this pressure, am I concentrating too much on my weaknesses and *forgetting my strengths?* Fifth, am I assuming that I can do nothing to *change* my situation? Finally, am I thinking pessimistically about the future rather than *tackling the present* in a constructive manner?

By asking some of these questions, we can clarify the task confronting us and 'restructure' the pressure as a challenge rather than as a threat.

In sport psychology, 'visualisation', or the imaginary rehearsal of a given skill before actually performing it, is a powerful technique for coping with competitive pressure. Briefly, research shows that people who combine physical with 'mental' practice (i.e., closing their eyes and 'seeing' and 'feeling' themselves executing skills successfully in their imagination) tend to be more confident of their abilities and perform skills significantly better than people whose only practice is physical. Theoretically, visualisation seems to work by allowing us to simulate in our mind the execution of a successful response to the anticipated danger. Repeated imagination of this response 'programmes' our mind for success. In other words, *what the mind can perceive, the body can achieve.*

Psychologically, mental rehearsal involves the controlled use of imagination. Accordingly, it is the exact opposite of anxiety where our imagination is out of control, threatening us with images of fear or failure.

Anecdotal testimonies to the benefits of mental rehearsal

abound among elite athletes – but sometimes, for rather unusual purposes. For example, consider how golfer, Nick Faldo, conquered a 'mental block' about landing a helicopter when learning to fly. Initially, he found that when flying the machine with the instructor, 'I just could not bring the helicopter down'. But over the next few weeks, he 'took time off in the privacy of my hotel room to spend 10 minutes simulating in my mind how to land the helicopter'. Through this systematic practice of visualisation, Faldo conquered his fear and became adept at landing the helicopter.

Recent years have seen increased interest in the use of mental imagery as a performance enhancement technique. Accordingly, commercial videotaped programmes of visualisation exercises are now available.

Most people respond pessimistically to pressure situations. For example, they may say to themselves such things as 'What a disaster! I'm finished' or 'It's hopeless! I'll never overcome this problem'. Unfortunately, because such comments are vague and self-critical, they create tension and feelings of futility within us. Conversely, if we give ourselves specific and positively-phrased instructions, we are more likely to take steps to tackle the problem confronting us. Accordingly, many cognitive behaviour modification theorists believe that what we say to ourselves (i.e., our 'self-talk') before, and during, stressful situations influences the success with which we handle pressure.

At least four stages of self-talk are usually required: preparation, confrontation, coping and self-reward. Let us now consider the purpose and nature of each of these stages.

(i) In the *preparatory* stage, one is encouraged to focus one's concentration only on the task to be performed, not on any irrelevant details:

* Let's see what exactly I have to do.
* I can work out a plan to handle this pressure.
* Just think about what I have to do – focus on actions not doubts.
* I've handled situations like this before.

(ii) The objective of the *confrontation* phase is to interpret feelings of tension as a signal to use one's coping techniques. So, the following self-statements are useful:

* I'm going to make my nervous energy work for me.
* One step at a time; I can handle this situation.
* Relax, I'm in control, take a deep breath.
* Look for positives; don't jump to conclusions.
* As long as I stay cool, I'll be in control.

(iii) In the *coping* stage, one's main aim is to stay in the present by saying such things as:

* When the pressure comes, just pause.
* Keep your focus on the present: what do I have to do now?
* Relax, breathe out and slow things down.
* It's time for problem solving.

(iv) The purpose of the *self-reward* stage is to praise oneself for any improvements in one's ability to face the pressure as compared with previous situations. Therefore, useful phrases here include:

* It worked. I was able to deal with it better than I'd expected.
* I made some progress and next time, I'll do even better.
* It gets easier every time I focus on the present.

In this chapter, we have explored some principles and techniques concerning the psychology of coping with competitive pressure. Perhaps the most important lesson to be learned from this analysis is the fact that people can learn to remain calm and focused in pressure situations by using such cognitive strategies as 'restructuring' the problem, visualising desired solutions and talking constructively to themselves while implementing them. So, despite what the Queen song proclaims, we do *not* have to be 'under pressure' throughout our lives!

Further Reading

Theoretical Material

Druckman, D. and Swets, J.A. (editors), *Enhancing Human Performance: Issues, Theories, and Techniques*, National Academy Press, Washington DC, 1988.

Jones, J.G. and Hardy, L. (eds), *Stress and Performance in Sport*, John Wiley, Chichester, 1990.

Rotella, R.J. and Lerner, J. D., 'Responding to Competitive Pressure', in R.N. Singer, M. Murphey & L. K. Tennant (eds), *Handbook of Research in Sport Psychology* (pp. 528–541), Macmillan, New York, 1993.

Whelan, J.P., Mahoney, M.J. & Meyers, A. W., 'Performance Enhancement in Sport: A Cognitive Behavioural Domain', *Behaviour Therapy*, 22, pp. 307–327, 1991.

Practical Books

Meichenbaum, D., *Stress Inoculation Training*, Pergamon, New York, 1985.

Orlick, T., *In Pursuit of Excellence* (Second Ed), Leisure Press, Champaign, Illinois, 1990.

Weinberg, R.S., *The Mental Advantage: Developing Your Psychological Skills in Tennis*, Human Kinetics, Champaign, Illinois, 1988.

FURTHER INFORMATION

If you require help you should contact your doctor or your local health centre or health board. They can deal with your problem directly or refer you to one of the many agencies, organisations, treatment centres or counselling services throughout the country.

For information on local support groups it may be useful to check with your community centre, health centre, citizens' information centre, or check the notice-boards at your parish church, your local library or at your doctor's office.

For emergency service numbers, consult the front pages of your local telephone directory.

The following are some useful contact numbers and addresses which provide free advice, referral or support. Many of the organisations have branches in towns and cities throughout the country. They will be happy to provide details on request.

The Editor

Bereavement

Irish Hospice Foundation, 64 Waterloo Road, Dublin 4. Phone: (01) 6603111, 6603639, 6603017.
Irish Sudden Infant Death Association, Carmichael House, 4 North Brunswick Street, Dublin 7. Phone: (01) 8747007.
Bereavement Counselling Service, c/o St Ann's Church, Dawson Street, Dublin 2. Phone: (01) 6767727.
National Association of Widows in Ireland, 12 Upper Ormond Quay, Dublin 7. Phone: (01) 6770977, 6770513.
Compassionate Friends, 18 Kilbarrack Avenue, Raheny, Dublin 5. Phone: (01) 8324618.

Addictions

Alcoholics Anonymous, 109 South Circular Road, Dublin 8. Phone: (01) 4538998.

Gamblers Anonymous, Carmichael House, North Brunswick Street, Dublin 7. Phone: (01) 8721133.

Overeaters Anonymous, PO Box 2529, Dublin 5. Phone: (01) 4515138.

Narcotics Anonymous, PO Box 1368, Sheriff Street, Dublin 1. Phone: (01) 8300944.

Al-Anon, 5 Capel Street, Dublin 1. Phone: (01) 8732699.

Alateen, 5 Capel Street, Dublin 1. Phone: (01) 8732699.

The Drug Treatment Centre Board, Trinity Court, 30/31 Pearse Street, Dublin 2. Phone: (01) 6771122.

The Family

Parentline: Organisation for Parents Under Stress, Carmichael House, North Brunswick Street, Dublin 7. Phone: (01) 8733500.

Family Mediation Service, Irish Life Centre, Block 1, Floor 5, Lower Abbey Street, Dublin 1. Phone: (01) 8728277, 8728708.

The Catholic Marriage Advisory Council, 39 Harcourt Street, Dublin 2. Phone: (01) 4780866.

Depression

AWARE-HELPLINE, 147 Phibsboro Road, Dublin 7. Phone: (01) 6791711.

Post-Traumatic Stress

Victim Support, 29/30 Dame Street, Dublin 2. Phone: (01) 6798673.

Panic/Agoraphobia

Out and About Association, 140 St Laurence's Road, Clontarf, Dublin 3. Phone: (01) 8338252, 8338253.

Schizophrenia

Schizophrenia Association of Ireland, 4 Fitzwilliam Place,

Dublin 2. Phone: (01) 6761988.

Children

Childline, c/o ISPCC, 20 Molesworth Street, Dublin 2. Phone: 1 800 666 666.

General

The Samaritans, 112 Marlborough Street, Dublin 1. Phone: (01) 8727700.
The Mental Health Association of Ireland, Mensana House, 6 Adelaide Street, Dún Laoghaire, Co. Dublin. Phone: (01) 2841166.

Further information is contained in the following useful publications:
The Irish Association for Counselling, *Guide to Counselling and Therapy: Directory,* Wolfhound Press, Dublin, 1991.
Directory of Alcohol, Drugs and Related Services in the Republic of Ireland, compiled by Sally Edwards, Golden Pages Ltd., November, 1992.

A booklet is also available from the Irish Association for Counselling containing a list of accredited counsellors and therapists throughout the country. The booklet can be obtained from: The Irish Association for Counselling, 9/11 Rockhill, Main Street, Blackrock, Co. Dublin. Phone: (01) 2780409.

More Interesting Books

Body-Mind Meditation
A Gateway to Spirituality

Louis Hughes, OP

You can take this book as your guide for a fascinating journey that need not take you beyond your own hall door. For it is an inward journey, and it will take you no further than God who, for those who want him as a friend, lives within. On the way to God-awareness, you will be invited to experience deep relaxation of body and mind.

Body-Mind Meditation can help you become a more integrated balanced person. It is an especially helpful approach to meditation if the pace of life is too fast for you, or if you find yourself frequently tense or exhausted.

An Easy Guide to Meditation

Roy Eugene Davis

Meditation is the natural process to use to release tension, reduce stress, increase awareness, concentrate more effectively and be open to life. In this book you will learn how to meditate correctly for inner growth and spiritual awareness. Specific guidelines are provided to assist the beginner as well as the more advanced meditator. Here are proven techniques used by accomplished meditators for years: *prayer, mantra, sound–light contemplation, ways to expand consciousness and to experience transcendence.*

Over 100,000 copies sold.

THE SPIRIT OF TONY DE MELLO
A Handbook of Meditation Exercises

John Callanan, SJ

This book captures the essence and spirit of Tony de Mello. He was a great teacher. Some said he was a dangerous one. He constantly challenged himself, the world within which he lived and those he came into contact with. For some this element of challenge was both unsettling and confusing. Tony said that our security does not lie in thoughts or ideas no matter how profound. Neither does it lie in traditions – no matter how hallowed. Security can only reside in an attitude of mind and a readiness to reflect deeply, thus subjecting any and every belief to rigorous questioning.

So Tony urged people to question, question, question. Questions often make us uncomfortable. They do, however, force us to reflect and thus ensure our growth.

John Callanan has started the book with an opening chapter on the basics of prayer. Then he moves on to try and give a flavour of the ideas and themes which gave so much zest and life to Tony de Mello's presentations. The exercises in this book are based on the prayer-style which Tony himself developed during his retreats.

SPIRITUALITY AND HOLISTIC LIVING

Sr. Theresa Feist

You are in search of wholeness. You have a body, mind and spiritual life. Your spirit cannot soar if your feet are heavy. Your mind is confused when your blood is stagnant. You need to care properly for your temple.

THE WAY OF A HEALER

Peter Gill

Introduction by Lilla Bek

THE WAY OF A HEALER deals with different aspects of healing, and the way that spiritual healing works in the lives of people. Healing means health, and health is wholeness. That word wholeness implies a number of separate parts coming together to make a complete whole. We are accustomed to the concept of body, mind and soul, and unless these different aspects of ourselves function together in harmony we have disharmony or dis-ease. If that condition of dis-ease is allowed to continue unchecked, ultimately we have disease or illness. Spiritual healing works at the physical, mental, emotional and spiritual levels of a person.

Today we stand upon the brink of the darkest age that could yet befall mankind, or, with a change of consciousness, upon the edge of a new and wonderful dawn to herald in a golden age. What that age will be depends upon what we make of it now. The immediate need is for a concept which will integrate us with the life of the solar system and, through the solar consciousness, link us with the life of the universe and the word of God. Our thinking must become much more expansive to embrace, not only humankind as we know it, but also the angel, elemental and nature kingdoms, and other realms not normally perceived by our physical sense.

Create Your Own Health Patterns

John L. Fitzpatrick, CSSp

Disease has to be understood in its literal sense dis-ease – a lack of ease and an expression of conflict. In general we create our own sickness and if we are capable of recreating our own sickness then we are capable or recreating our own health. Once inner peace and harmony are re-established nature has the power to repair itself and good health should ensue.

The Jobs Crisis

Edited by Colm Keane

The list of well-known and highly regarded contributors to this RTE Thomas Davis lecture series includes Colm McCarthy, Dr Garrett Fitzgerald, Mike Allen, Raymond Crotty, Peter Cassells, Gearóid Ó Tuathaigh, J. J. Lee, Brendan Halligan, Brendan Walsh, David Kennedy, Paddy Walley, John Kenneth Galbraith and Colm Keane. Their lectures will be of interest to a broad range of people – academics, politicians, policy makers, administrators, students, and anyone affected by unemployment.